*My Cat is Driving Me Crazy!*

*Also by Grace Mc Hatty*

The Cat Maintenance Manual

The Cat Maintenance Log

Problem Cat

Supercat

The Going Live! Cat Book

That's Cats

Your Natural Cat (with Tim Couzens)

Kitten Care for Children

The Cat Lover's Dictionary

# My Cat is Driving Me Crazy!

**An Owner's Guide to Cat Care with Natural Remedies**

Grace Mc Hatty and
Tim Couzens
BVetMed, MRCVS, VetMFHom

CARROLL & GRAF PUBLISHERS, INC.
New York

Carroll & Graf Publishers, Inc.
260 Fifth Avenue
New York
NY 10001

First published in the UK by Robinson Publishing Ltd 1995

First Carroll & Graf edition 1995

Illustrations by E. J. Fairbairn

ISBN 0–7867–0160–9

Printed and bound in Great Britain

10 9 8 7 6 5 4 3 2 1

# *Contents*

# *Introduction: Choosing a Natural Remedy*

Anyone who has kept a cat for any length of time comes to know immediately when it is unwell or in pain, and can take it to their vet confident in the knowledge that, for many illnesses and injuries at least, conventional cures are at hand. However, when your cat's behaviour goes awry and seems to be persistently wayward and out of control – whether it is spraying curtains, ripping furniture, munching its way through your best jerseys, or diving for cover when anyone comes to your home – then you must consider what course to take.

First, it goes without saying, always check with your vet to make sure that there *is* no underlying physical cause why your cat seems to be acting so perversely and in such an attention-seeking way. If the vet pronounces your cat physically fit, yet it continues to be cross-grained, despondent, listless or down-right aggressive, think hard about your cat's circumstances, and think hard whether there are outside factors affecting its behaviour that can be changed.

Cats love routine; they don't like their territory disturbed or mealtimes changed, or even the type of food they eat. They don't like their particular patch invaded, and are terrified by visitations to their garden from the local unneutered tom; car journeys also take them out of their territory, and so, of course, does moving house. They won't like visits to catteries, or cat shows (unless they are very accustomed to them), or their owner's prolonged absence on holiday, or being left alone all day. If they are kept indoors, with little company, are not played with, and have nothing to entertain them, they will be bored out of their whiskers. So look at life from their point of view, and examine your own way of life, to see whether there are ways of alleviating their seemingly delinquent behaviour by altering *yours* first. This applies particularly to many new owners of cats who, in all innocence, may not have realized that cats need much more than good quality food and a warm home. So if you are out at work all day and have only one cat, confined to your flat, realize that this is very like solitary confinement in a prison for a cat. Cats need companionship, and they need mental stimulation, so think about getting yours a companion cat, or at least toys to play with and a more stimulating environment. (Cats can derive endless pleasure from a catnip mouse, and a cardboard box can provide an exciting place to hide and jump in and out of, for example.) But, above all, make sure you spend some time every day playing with your cat, stroking it and showing it affection.

Most delinquent behaviour stems from stress, distress and sheer boredom. Each section of this book will explore some of the underlying reasons. Sometimes the circumstances causing them can be ameliorated, sometimes not, but it is always possible to help alleviate your cat's distress through using the natural remedies of alternative medicine detailed in this book: herbalism, homoeopathy, Bach flower remedies and aromatherapy – therapies that have proved beneficial to humans sometimes for centuries, and which have been adapted now for feline use.

Read them carefully and see which one seems most closely suited to your cat and its particular type of behaviour. And, *please*, before embarking on any of them, always refer to the sections on dosages given in the Introductions to the therapies and how to administer them (pp. 5, 8–10, 12, 15–16). Since some of the plants listed are poisonous if taken in excess, *never exceed the prescribed dose which will be quite harmless if used correctly* and will, indeed, be beneficial, as you will see.


## HERBALISM

When animals living in the wild are sick, they often instinctively seek out plants to heal themselves. And cats, although they are by nature carnivores, when allowed out of doors will eat grass; indeed, they need grass as an aid to digestion and to make themselves sick in order to get rid of hair balls or anything else unsuitable that they have swallowed. So, if your cat lives indoors, make sure that it has a supply of grass, which you can grow in a pot on the windowsill. If you can get cocksfoot grass – their favourite – so much the better. Without grass your cat may resort to eating the pot plants, which may be poisonous and certainly won't help it. This is just a simple illustration of how cats enterprisingly treat themselves.

Herbs, some rightly, some wrongly, have been used for medicinal purposes for over 4,000 years; much of the knowledge gained over the centuries relating to their healing powers has been recorded in herbals, the most famous being John Gerard's of 1597 and Nicholas Culpeper's of 1653. In the eighteenth century Europeans began to turn to other methods of cure, but herbs have continued to play an extremely important role in both Chinese and North American Indian medicine. Some 85 per cent of the world's human population still rely on herbalism for their basic health today. As time has passed we have learnt how to refine some of the older remedies – omitting those that were thought curative simply because the shape of the plant resembled the shape of the organ they were intended to cure!

Vets too once used herbal remedies extensively, in fact right up to the earlier part of this century. The advent of seemingly more powerful drugs was responsible for their fall from favour. But the tide is turning: more and more veterinary surgeons and pet owners alike are realizing that age-old traditional remedies still have a part to play in the treatment of domestic pets.

All herbal remedies are made up of a complex mixture of ingredients, and orthodox medicine has isolated and copied many of the active compounds, producing many modern drugs we take for granted, such as digitalis and aspirin, but it does not take into account one of herbalism's most fundamental and vital aspects. All the components in an individual plant-based remedy are balanced, as nature intended, working together, smoothing out any potential side-effects and enhancing each other's actions. This means that most herbal remedies are safe. While some must only be used under expert guidance, all the remedies included in this book have been used regularly on domestic pets for many, many years without any problems.

Herbal remedies normally work in a very subtle way, gently acting in harmony with the body and not against it. For this reason they often appear to be working only slowly, sometimes taking several weeks to achieve their full effect. Once you can see your cat responding, then you can often reduce the dose to a maintenance level for more long-term treatment.

By far the easiest and cheapest source for herbal remedies is your local pet shop. There are commercial companies who produce herbal remedies for domestic pets including products which contain many of the herbs given in the text, and a list of stockists is given at the end of the book.

### *Dosages*

*Herbal remedies usually come as tablets with the correct dose given on the side of the packaging, and it is important to follow this.*

*In some cases where herbs are not commercially available in tablet form, you can prepare them yourself.*

*The quickest and simplest way is to prepare an infusion from dried herbs which are available over the counter, or by mail order. This is a bit like making tea, you can even use a small teapot if you wish.*

*To make a standard infusion add half a cupful of boiling water to half a teaspoon of dried herb and leave to stand for 15 minutes. Strain the mixture and leave to cool. If you want to combine more than one herb together (which is often done to increase effectiveness), then add equal parts of all the ingredients together, but still do not use more than half a teaspoon of mixture to make your infusion.*

*Infusions will keep in the fridge for a few days if kept in a dark bottle and tightly stoppered. The average dose for an adult cat is between 2 to 3 teaspoons three times daily added to food.*

*Most herbs do not have a very pleasant flavour, and most cats will object if you try to give the remedies straight into the mouth. For tips on how to trick your cat into taking its medicine, see Administering the Remedy on pp. 15–16.*

*It is generally not wise to treat pregnant or very young animals with herbal remedies, unless under specialist guidance.*

*Dose your cat daily until you notice it is responding. Usually this will take up to about ten days, after which you can sometimes halve the dose for more long-term treatment. With most remedies the treatment can gradually be phased out after two or three months as the cat adapts to the situation. Seek the advice of a vet if you intend to continue herbal treatment for more than four or five months.*

## HOMOEOPATHY

Although the principle of homoeopathy dates back to the Ancient Greeks, it was with the pioneering work of the German physician Samuel Hahnemann that its potential became realized. The whole basis of homoeopathy is founded on the theory that 'like can cure like'. The idea is that by a remedy provoking symptoms similar to the illness it seeks to cure, it stimulates the body's own healing process. Hahnemann took some twenty years testing his hypothesis, using a great number of substances on himself and friends. In each case he carefully noted down the symptoms, both physical and mental, which developed as a result of taking each individual remedy. These he compiled in his own *Materia Medica* and by listing what a substance could cause, he was aware of what it was capable of curing.

Hahnemann knew that some of the remedies he tested were toxic, so he set about finding the minimum dose needed for a cure. He began diluting his remedies, finding as he did so that the more diluted they were the more effective they became as medicines. (This is, of course, in direct contrast to modern drugs which become less effective when diluted.) His discovery that infinitely diluted substances could be used to heal meant that some of the most poisonous substances known could be put to use therapeutically, without worrying about their toxic nature.

Today almost any substance can be prepared homoeopathically, even metals, minerals, snake venoms and diseased tissue. Unlike herbal remedies, however, it is not something that can be attempted at home, and you should rely on trusted stockists for your supplies (see p. 133). Your remedy will most likely come in pill form. The homoeopathic pills that are on sale commercially are so diluted that they do not contain any of the original substance. Instead, they contain energy derived from the substance and it is this which stimulates the body to heal. Take, as an example, Arnica 30 (or 30c), a remedy frequently used for animals when injured or in a state of shock. These would be prepared initially from an alcoholic extract of the plant, known as the mother tincture. One drop of this would be added to 99 drops of an alcohol/water mixture and the test tube shaken vigorously. The contents of this tube contain the first centesimal potency, or a '1c' dilution. One drop of this would then be added to 99 drops of alcohol/water mixture and once again this would be shaken, giving the '2c' potency. This process would be repeated a further 28 times before the 30c potency is achieved. A few drops of the required potency is then added to lactose tablets or powders, which then become potentized with the active remedy.

Looking at the process scientifically, a dilution even at the 6c potency is equivalent to 1:1,000,000,000,000, more or less one drop of mother tincture in the combined volume of 50 swimming pools. Critics say that it is difficult to see how such remedies can act, yet homoeopathy has proved effective in treating a wide variety of problems in animals where the number of successes lies outside the realms of chance. It seems that the weaker the solution the higher the potency.

Correctly applied, homoeopathy can be a remarkable and effective system of medicine which has the benefit of being safe and having no side-effects. The remedies can be used to treat the youngest kitten to the oldest cat without fear of doing any harm. However, in order for homoeopathy to succeed, the remedy must be matched to your cat's symptoms fairly accurately. The closer the match, the more likely your cat's chance of a response. If by chance the wrong remedy is given, then nothing will happen, but neither will any harm have been done.

### *Dosages*

*When you read the various sections in this book, look closely at the homoeopathic remedies and try to choose the one which matches best your cat's problem, personality and general characteristics. Remember that although behaviour is the key element, homoeopathic prescribing looks at the cat as a whole and takes into account such factors as likes or dislikes, appetite, thirst, physical build and even how symptoms can vary with the time of day.*

*Having selected your remedy you will discover that they are available in various strengths or potencies. The most common remedies you will find in chemist's and, or better still in health food shops, in the 6c or 30c potency (although the 'c' is usually dropped from the front of the packaging). The less frequently used remedies you will need to order from a specialist homoeopathic pharmacy; see the suppliers' list at the back of the book (p. 133).*

*Choice of remedy is important and so is selection of the potency. Low potencies, such as 6c, have relatively little healing energy and frequent doses are needed to produce a result. One advantage of using these, however, is that the match between the remedy and your cat's symptoms does not have to be quite so exact. Slightly higher potencies, such as 30c, have more inherent healing power, need fewer doses to produce an effect and heal at a deeper level, at the expense of having to be more accurately matched to your cat. Even higher potencies such as 200c or 1M have a profound healing action and often need only a few doses to produce remarkable results, but the match with the symptoms has to be spot on, or the remedy will not work.*

*As far as the homoeopathic remedies given in this book are concerned, as a general rule start with the 6c potency. Give it four times daily for seven to ten days.*

*If you feel that there is some improvement in the situation, then increase the potency to 30c, but dose only twice daily for about one week.*

*If the remedy seems to be working well, carry on with the 30c potency until you feel the situation is under control.*

*If the effect of the remedy appears to wear off after a few days and the cat relapses, change to the 200c potency given three times weekly or try the 1M potency given once or twice weekly, depending on the result.*

*Where there is no change in your cat's condition, either try another homoeopathic remedy or switch therapies.*

*Remedies are available in various forms: tablets (either soft or hard), granules, powders and drops. As 'energized' medicines they need special care, handling and storage. They are easily deactivated by strong smells and vapours such as camphor and eucalyptus. They should be stored well away from any aromatherapy products. Bright light, heat and electromagnetic radiation (e.g. from TVs and computers) can also deactivate or depotentize them, rendering them useless. Stored properly though, the remedies will keep for many years without losing their efficacy.*

*Tablets are the most readily available form and are cheapest. The one drawback with tablets is the fact that they should not be handled as this can depotentize them. Carefully tip the remedy onto the bottle lid and from here into your cat's mouth (see Administering the Remedy for tips on how to do this pp. 15–16). If this is not practical (and we all know how difficult cats can be), then try hiding the tablet in food. If this doesn't work then carefully crush up a tablet in a folded piece of white paper. This can then be tipped into the mouth or onto food. You will find that the soft lactose tablets will crush up much easier than the harder (more common) type.*

*As an alternative you can buy ready potentized powders from a homoeopathic pharmacy. This saves you the time and trouble of crushing tablets but is more expensive. The pharmacy will*

(cont.)

(cont.)

*also prepare potentized sucrose granules of your chosen remedy for you. These are cheaper than powders, and you should use about 10 granules as a single dose to replace a tablet or powder. Some people use liquid potencies which are prepared in alcohol. You may find this more difficult to use as many cats are able to detect this, even though a dose (equivalent to a tablet or powder) is only 3 or 4 drops of the remedy added to either food or water each time.*

*In rare cases a homoeopathic remedy can aggravate a condition, i.e., make it worse before it gets better. This is usually considered a good sign, but it is best in this situation to cease treatment for 24 hours before starting again. If you are worried, then it is best to seek advice from a veterinary surgeon familiar with homoeopathic principles.*

*Finally, you will need to decide how long to treat your cat. If your cat has lost its companion, and is pining, for example, this is a relatively short-term problem and will probably need treatment over a period of 1 or 2 weeks to alleviate the situation. Long-term behavioural problems, such as aggression or spraying, on the other hand, will need repeated courses of treatment on either a daily or weekly basis.*

## BACH FLOWER REMEDIES

This form of treatment is becoming more popular as time passes, and has been used to treat a variety of psychological problems. These remedies are not limited to humans, in fact we are only just realizing the potential they have in helping all variety of animals, including cats of course.

They are named after their pioneer, Dr Edward Bach, a famous physician who lived between 1886 and 1936. This simple, natural method of healing uses flowers. Bach realized a link between emotional states and actual physical illness. His remedies were devised to treat such problems indirectly, getting to the root of many diseases by dealing with the underlying psychological imbalances. His flower remedies provide a subtle way of healing, bearing some similarities to both homoeopathy and herbalism, yet not acting directly, but at levels which influence the body's energies.

No one knows for sure how the remedies work, but energy is involved in a form which we cannot as yet measure. Each flower used contains energy of a particular wavelength and it is thought that these 'tune in' with the energy field that surrounds every living animal or human. Bach saw an internal conflict between the animal's soul and personality (which nowadays we interpret as behavioural changes and problems), and saw the energy field becoming distorted and out of harmony, thus having a negative effect on the whole animal. Appropriate flower remedies containing the harmonious energy frequencies act as healing catalysts to rectify the deviations.

All Bach remedies are based on flowers except one, ROCK WATER, which is made from natural spring water, which has its own inherent energy. The flowerheads are picked at full maturity when the essential energies are concentrated, then floated on water, transferring their energy to the liquid. A few drops of energized water are added to brandy (which acts as a preservative) to produce stock solutions for medication. The normal dilution is 1:240 water to brandy. These stock bottles will keep indefinitely and each contains a small pipette to measure out the drops.

Altogether there are 38 different remedies, covering almost every state of mind, and one combined remedy, RESCUE REMEDY, which is the best known of all the Bach flower remedies. They are safe to use in any situation and for any age of cat, as there are no side-effects. Even if the wrong remedy is given no harm will come to the animal. Where necessary, several remedies can be combined to cover all the various aspects of a particular problem.

### *Dosages*

*There are several different ways of giving the remedies. The easiest is in your cat's drinking water. Each day add 2 or 3 drops of each of your chosen remedy or remedies to the water. As the amounts used are small compared to the volume of drinking water, the remedies should not be detectable. If your cat does not drink from an inside bowl, then add the remedies to the food instead. Try to dose 4 times each day, using titbits if necessary to dose between meal times.*

*Another way of using the remedies is to dilute them in water by making a treatment bottle. Put two drops of each remedy into a bottle containing about 30ml still spring water and add 1 teaspoon of cider vinegar as a preservative. Dose your cat with 4 drops of this 4 times each day. Once again this can be added to the food if necessary. If you plan to use Rescue Remedy in this way then add 4 drops to your treatment bottle instead of 2.*

*In an emergency the remedies can be given undiluted, straight from the stock bottle, into the mouth, but do try to avoid contaminating the end of the pipette. Since the remedies are prepared in brandy, some cats may object to the taste, although remember that you only need to give a drop or two to be effective.*

*Bach remedies are often slow to work and you may need to carry on treatment for some weeks or months to achieve complete resolution of the problem.*

*Finally, if you are really stuck and there is no other way to give the treatment, then neat remedy can be gently rubbed into the skin (inside the thigh area is best) or onto the lips. This works well in acute accident situations.*

## AROMATHERAPY

Aromatherapy is a system of healing that has existed for thousands of years; it utilizes essential aromatic oils derived from plants. Of late, it has become popular for humans and, not surprisingly, this has led to its use on animals, albeit on a much, much smaller scale. The use of oils is based largely on observation, allowing various properties to be ascribed to each individual oil. Each essential oil has its own unique fragrance and healing properties. However the way oils act is probably far more complex than might at first appear, involving absorption into the body and then healing by influencing the body's meridians in some way.

Essential oils are produced by distilling the original plant material, that sometimes yields only a few millilitres of oil from a seemingly vast quantity of foliage. This makes oils fairly expensive, but this is offset by the fact that only very small amounts are used therapeutically.

---

### Application

***These oils are never given internally.*** *They are applied in two ways. The first uses an electric or candle-powered burner to evaporate the oil, so that your cat can inhale it. You will probably find an electric vaporizer a lot safer, as your cat cannot overturn it. Some shops sell small rings to fit over light bulbs, so that the heat from the lamp can vaporize the oil. These are cheap but after a time become sticky, hairy and dusty.*

*Sometimes you can use oils without a vaporizer by sprinkling small amounts of certain neat oils inside your cat's basket or onto bedding. Not all oils are suitable for use in this way, and advice is given in the relevant sections on which oils are appropriate.*                                                      (cont.)

(cont.)

*If you are going to use a vaporizer place it in the same room as your cat and close the door. Fill the vaporizer bowl with a little water and then carefully add a few drops of neat oil. As this evaporates in the gentle heat, it is absorbed through the lungs into the bloodstream and then passes on to the brain where it can act.*

*The second way of applying oils is through massage. Most cats enjoy this. However, it's important to bear in mind that these oils are very concentrated, extremely potent and when used for massage they should never be used undiluted unless special directions are given. Neat oils can cause severe skin reactions, such as blistering, and irritate mucous membranes. Large amounts of undiluted oil can also be toxic and may cause liver or kidney damage since they are absorbed so rapidly through the skin into the bloodstream.*

*Before using these oils for massage, it is normal practice to dilute them in a carrier oil. Base oils most commonly used include sweet almond, johoba, wheat germ or sunflower, all of which can be easily obtained, but sweet almond seems the most appropriate as it is relatively cheap and not too greasy.*

*When diluting the oils for massage add 1 drop of oil to 2 ml of carrier, giving a 2.5 per cent dilution. Make up a small amount for use and store in a well-stoppered amber glass bottle out of bright sunlight, in a cool place.*

*Put two or three drops of diluted oil onto your fingertips and massage carefully and gently into the skin on the inside of your cat's thigh where there is relatively little hair. Five minutes' massage at the most should be sufficient to allow the oils to penetrate through the skin. Doing this twice daily should be enough to help in most cases.*

Each individual oil can contain over 100 different chemical constituents. Because of their complex nature, natural oils are far more effective than their synthetic counterparts. Look closely at what you buy and try to use only organically produced natural oils. Buy only very small quantities, replacing your stock as needed. Even in a well-stoppered bottle most undiluted oils will only keep for two years at the most. Citrus type oils will remain potent for even less time, usually about six months. Blended, diluted oils will only keep well for about three months, after that they become less effective.

## ADMINISTERING THE REMEDY

Cats, as we all know, are some of the most cunning creatures alive, never more so when it comes to the vital administering of any form of medicine. An acquaintance tells me of her problems when trying to give her two cats just the routine worming tablets – even though they are described as 'palatable' on the packaging. She manages, she says, to pop the tablets into her cats' mouths. Both her cats pretend to swallow, but in fact are still holding them in their mouths, and minutes later will discreetly deposit them in some hidden corner, only to be found hours after their owner had congratulated herself on their successful administration. Various ploys have been tried since – concealing them in butter, even Marmite, and popping them in, or just throwing them on to the floor as a game: each ploy has worked successfully just once.

But, actually, there is no need to get into a tizzy about dosing your cats, and certainly, if you feel alarmed yourself, your cat will sense it and be on the alert.

There is a simple effective way, though, admittedly, it is easier with two people present than with just one person coping on her own. For that reason, I will describe it as though you are on your own.

- Have a towel handy, and the pills at the ready on a firm table.

- Capture your cat, and quickly wrap the towel round its entire body including paws, leaving only the head free.

- Place its bottom firmly on the table, with its body facing away from you, its back tucked against you.

- Using your left forearm to hold the cat in place, gently use your left hand to squeeze the sides of its jaw. Normally, it will now open its mouth; if it doesn't, place a nail of your other hand on its bottom teeth and pull down.

- With your free hand, pop the pill to the back of its throat. Shut its mouth, then gently massage its throat till it swallows. Alternatively you can blow on its nose or touch the tip of its nose for the same result.

- For administering drops of liquid, you will find a medicine dropper easier to use than a teaspoon. Use this same method to use the dropper (without the throat massage). Should this method fail or you haven't a dropper, try putting the medicine mixed with some cream cheese or butter on the cat's paws. Cats hate having tacky paws and will lick it off.

Bear in mind too that cats can be tricked into eating almost anything if you are as cunning as they are: try to let them think they are stealing it!

# Cats with Abnormal Cravings

Cats who start to eat things most normal cats consider inedible or unpalatable are worrying, and it is worth consulting your vet immediately. Sometimes cats will suddenly start consuming their cat litter, licking concrete or eating soil. Usually this is a sign or symptom of serious illness, such as liver disease, toxoplasmosis or leukaemia. And only your vet can offer you advice and treatment on this, as it is beyond the scope of this book.

There is, however, a much more common category of cats with bizarre eating habits, and as the owners of such cats will testify, their tastes are 'expensive'! These strange habits are psychologically based, rather than a symptom of physical illness. I received a letter from a worried owner of a Siamese, who ate dishcloths! At first she tried hiding clothes, towels and dishcloths from him, but then had to give in. Whenever he has a meal now, he has a mouthful of catfood, followed by a mouthful of old sweater. I have also heard of another owner who lost several very good cashmere sweaters this way! The most common offenders are Orientals, mostly Siamese, but Burmese are fairly well represented as well. Crossbreeds can also be affected. Most people believe that such cats probably have some Oriental in their background. Items commonly consumed include wool (very popular), clothing (especially after it has been worn), carpet, furniture covering, elastic bands, electrical wiring (dangerous) and plants (poisonous). Various causes have been suggested, but some people think that it is a genetic trait, as several members of a litter may be found doing this. Stress, trauma, illness, change in daily routine, moving house or the introduction of a new cat can all trigger this behaviour. If your cat started doing this early in life it may have been because it was separated from its mother too early on, and missed out on its emotional development.

How your cat will respond to treatment will vary, depending on whether or not you can pinpoint the cause. Different therapies can be combined along with dietary management. Try feeding dried pelleted cat food. This does seem to help, and an advantage is that it can be left down all day, allowing ad-lib feeding. This not only distracts the offender from chewing your best jumper, but makes the stomach feel full at the same time, with less room for your favourite socks.

**Herbal Remedies** (see p. 5 for dosages and pp. 15–16 for administration)

There are two remedies to help here, not to be taken internally but to provide a distraction. Get your cat a toy containing CATNIP (Catmint, *Nepeta cataria*). Cats love these toys and become very attached to them. They will spend hours happily playing with them. Less commonly known is the irresistible desire that cats have for VALERIAN root (*Valeriana officinalis*) Although this smells somewhat foul to us, cats find it extremely attractive. Leaving toys filled with either herb around will help in some cases, and provide alternative entertainment to chewing the light flex.

**Homoeopathic Remedies** (see pp. 8–10 for dosages and pp. 15–16 for administration)

IGNATIA (St Ignatius bean, *Ignatia amara*) If there is any one remedy (other than PLATINA) which matches the personality of a Siamese cat, then it is Ignatia, which, incidentally, as a remedy is more suited to females, but will actually work in either sex.

Ignatia cats are highly emotional (and vocal). Mood varies and is subject to rapid change: happy and affectionate one minute, then sullen, miserable and irritable the next; one moment sitting on your lap devouring attention, and moments later hiding under the bed hissing, fending off any advances with vigour, trying to devour you! They are extremely sensitive to stress, particularly emotional stress, such as shock, grief, pining and resentment. Such emotions are often pent up, leading to brooding, ill-humour or a change in behaviour. This includes eating wool and other such indigestible materials. Also characteristic is a low tolerance to pain, as demonstrated by the classic Siamese cry often heard after any sort of surgical intervention however minor, and there is also a marked dislike of tobacco smoke, which means that such a cat will leave the room when you light up.

NITRICUM ACIDUM (Nitric acid) The character of the cat patient who suits this remedy is often irritable (and even more bad tempered in hot weather). Owners will report that they are difficult cats to care for generally, due to their obstinate nature. They are sensitive to noise, and enjoy eating salty fish.

CALC. CARB. (Calcium carbonate, chalk) The type of cat for whom this is suitable is easy to spot: the cat who seems sluggish, dull, lazy and overweight, for whom everything is so much of an effort, even thinking, let alone moving around. They are sometimes subject to odd phobias and fears and may even startle at sudden noises. At the opposite end of the scale shouting and gentle prodding may fail to get the offending feline dislodged from the most comfortable armchair – they love warmth and comfort. They will eat various odd items, the more indigestible the better. Less rotund cats of this nature will often respond better to CALC. PHOS. (calcium phosphate) than calc. carb.

ALUMINA (Aluminium oxide) Cold is not appreciated by cats suited by this remedy, who are more often than not found in the warmest of places. They are hurried in their movements, in contrast to the tardy calc. carb. type cat. Their skin tends to be rather dry and the nails somewhat brittle, cracking easily. As far as eating preferences go, clothing is particularly favoured.

**Bach Flower Remedies** (see p. 12 for dosages and pp. 15–16 for their administration)

CHICORY (*Cichorium intybus*) If, besides its abnormal eating habits your cat seems over-possessive towards you and over-demanding emotionally, this remedy may suit it. Does your cat show signs of insecurity when you leave for work? Do its strange dietary obsessions such as eating wool or chewing the carpet take place only when you are absent? Where over-bonding is clearly the problem, chicory will help immensely.

HONEYSUCKLE (*Lonicera caprifolium*) Homesickness is a keynote here. Honeysuckle will help cats who start craving indigestible materials when either staying in a boarding cattery or after moving house. They are not able to come to terms with the emotions associated with the current changes in their lives and start this bizarre behaviour to try to comfort themselves. Honeysuckle removes such feelings and helps the cat come to accept the present situation.

WALNUT (*Juglans regia*) Walnut is a little like HONEYSUCKLE. It helps in adjusting to changes in life. There are some important differences however. WALNUT is needed where there is difficulty in coping with actual changes such as moving house or the introduction of a new cat. On the other hand honeysuckle deals with the actual feelings associated with leaving behind either familiar or favourite surroundings or someone (be it cat or human) with which there is a bond.

STAR OF BETHLEHEM (*Ornithogalum umbellatum*) If your cat has been through a recent trauma, such as being trapped in a shed, or involved in a car accident, or has had a severe fright of some kind, occasionally obsessional cravings will start after such events. This is due to suppressed emotions. Use Star of Bethlehem even if the triggering event was some time in the past.

WILD ROSE (*Rosa canina*) Modern-day cats vary quite considerably in lifestyle from their wild-living or feral counterparts. In the wild much of a cat's day would have been involved in hunting and killing prey and then consuming it. All this would have taken time. The modern-day consequence of this is boredom which is quite simply because we do most of the work by providing instant food. Fabric-chewing is understandably a distraction and occupies some of the day. It may be some way of simulating the way in which a cat would tear up and chew its prey in the wild. Wild rose may help here. It is indicated in apathy and general lack of interest in life (i.e. bored with life) and can induce feelings of vitality and enthusiasm.

**Aromatherapy** (see pp. 13–14 for application)

In this instance aromatherapy would not be used directly on the cat, but rather on your garments, to act as a deterrent to ward off would-be chewers. Use EUCALYPTUS (*Eucalyptus globulus*) and PEPPERMINT (*Mentha piperita*) which both seem to work well. Sprinkle a drop or two of oil onto the intended item. In many instances the vapour is sufficiently pungent to ward off the most fervent consumers.

# Belligerent Cats

Aggression is a common problem for dog-owners to have to deal with. However, most vets will tell you that they see an almost endless string of cats, bearing a variety of painful tooth- or claw-marks on various parts of their anatomy: the result of fighting which sometimes can be quite serious.

Aggression can be quite normal sometimes. You will notice a certain degree of aggression if your cat catches prey and plays with it. There is nothing wrong with this unless taken to extremes, and your cat annihilates all wildlife coming anywhere near the house. If this happens, try feeding fresh food rather than tinned. This is one step closer to nature and a move away from 'ready meals' by providing the cat with something to take the place of the self-service department outside. It also helps to feed the cat just before it is allowed out so that its stomach is full and it will therefore feel less hungry.

A cat may also snarl while it is eating its food. Many cats don't like being touched while they are eating, so don't do it. Leave the cat alone, food guarding is a natural instinct. However, if your cat is really aggressive in this way, you could try feeding less desirable foods, particularly those which are less aromatic, like dry pelleted food.

Most cats will aggressively defend their territory and confront any threatening challenge. This is also normal unless the behaviour gets out of hand and the cat actively seeks out neighbouring cats and attacks them. Neutering is important in controlling this type of behaviour.

*Don't mistake rough play for aggression. Lucy, a blue British short-hair cross was adopted, as a kitten, from a feral colony to provide company for an elderly cat called Eric. Out in the garden she took a fiendish delight in lying in ambush for him, leaping on him as he sauntered unsuspectingly across the garden and digging her claws in, yet indoors she always deferred to him, allowing him to eat from the cat dish first.*

Be wary. Unlike a dog who lies on its back as an act of submission, a cat lies on its back as the optimum position for fighting, as this leaves all its claws free as well as its sharp teeth. Tickling their tummies in this position can lead to triggering the 'fight mode', when they suddenly can no longer resist grasping your hand with all four paws and digging in their claws.

Some types of aggression are actually learned through bad experiences, particularly unwanted attention from young

*An acquaintance tells us of a house-warming party she attended. Outside the new residence, was a low wall, and on it a beautiful tabby (not the hostess's), lying invitingly on its back. 'What a dear little cat,' my acquaintance said, unable to resist giving its tummy a tickle. Wham! Her hand was instantly encased in four sets of steel claws, and she eventually withdrew it, dripping with blood. 'Oh dear,' said her hostess, as she entered her house. 'You're the third one it has happened to this evening.' Others arrived one by one, all clutching their scratches: in fact a total of ten. When everyone left for home, the strange cat had gone, and was never seen again.*

children. In these circumstances most cats will run away, but a few will stand and fight. The next time the situation arises they will anticipate the situation and attack first. Sometimes unusual aggressive behaviour is misdirected towards the owner. The root of the problem is basically anger and the only way the seething feline can vent its feelings is to let fly. Tortoiseshell or tabbies seem prone to this type of behaviour.

In addition to the remedies mentioned below there is evidence that diet can have some bearing on a cat's behaviour. Some cats are food-sensitive, particularly to certain types of protein or to various additives such as preservatives or antioxidants. Where the cause of the aggression cannot be identified it may well be worth changing to an additive-free diet for a while to see if this helps.

**Herbal Remedies** (see p. 5 for dosages and pp. 15–16 for administration)

Herbal remedies with calming properties can help some particularly aggressive hyperactive cats. Combinations of VALERIAN, SKULLCAP and HOPS (see p. 126) seem to be effective and can be used long term if need be.

**Homoeopathic Remedies** (see pp. 8–10 for dosages and pp. 15–16 for administration)

HYOSCYAMUS (Henbane) is most effective in treating aggression *per se*. Use it for territorial-based aggression and in treating those cats who go on raiding sorties to antagonize neighbouring cats.

Hyoscyamus-type cats are often aggressive by nature and prone to fits of violence. They are fearful, jealous and suspicious, ardently defending their territory, attacking any poor unsuspecting cat who trespasses on their patch. Revenge is swift and powerful, often wounding the opponent severely.

BELLADONNA (Deadly nightshade) belongs to the same plant family as HYOSCYAMUS. Cats for whom belladonna is suited share the aggressive trait. Fear is less prominent, but fury and violent temper abound, with sudden lashing out with sharpened claws and needle-like teeth. Senses are very acute and the cat starts at the least noise or sudden movement. This is likely to result in an unsuspecting owner being bitten.

NUX VOMICA (Poison nut) Active, lean cats who feel the cold can be nux vomica types. They are usually tense and over-anxious, malicious individuals, with a disposition to pick a fight or quarrel. Their irritable nature must have an outlet. Outbursts of rage are not uncommon, after which they feel much better. They are always on the move, constantly checking that everything is in order. They have a voluptuous appetite yet never seem to put on much weight.

LACHESIS (Bushmaster snake venom) Fear or dislike of being touched is one of the characteristics of cats suited to lachesis. Lachesis can be used to help cats who resent interference and will suddenly lash out for no real reason. Especially touchy areas include the throat and abdomen. Lachesis often suits anxious, suspicious females and they can be sensitive, ego-centric and conceited individuals. New cats entering the household and upsetting the balance and harmony can cause jealousy, leading to a little local social conflict.

HEPAR SULPH. (Calcium sulphide) is commonly used to treat abscesses and infected wounds. It finds another use in helping ferocious, extremely irritable individuals that have underlying feelings of dejection and sadness. This means a quarrelsome nature that does not like to be interfered with or unduly upset. They are animals who feel the cold and like to hide under warm blankets or bed covers.

LYCOPODIUM (Club moss) Somewhat prickly at times and on occasion gentle and subdued, cats who benefit from lycopodium are basically self-conscious, shy and apprehensive. Aggression is manifested as sudden bouts of temper unleashed without warning. Past insults or injuries are remembered with feelings of resentment and a desire for revenge. Opposition from a rival is not at all appreciated. Lycopodium cats either have a picky, fussy appetite or will eat everything in sight and then ask for more. They rarely gain weight no matter how much food they consume. Fear of being touched, picked up or approached by strangers can be a feature.

TARENTULA HISPANIA (Spanish spider) Cats who are cunning and crafty and prone to sudden aggressive urges, although their underlying nature often reveals that they are timid will benefit from this remedy. They do not easily tolerate others entering their territory which incites violent outbursts. When discontented and angry their attacks can be very intense in nature, inflicting severe injuries on the victim.

CHAMOMILLA (German chamomile) See page 31 for a description of the angry type of cat suited to chamomile.
   Chamomile is useful where pain induces this type of behaviour in otherwise normal cats. Pain-induced aggression can arise after surgery where remedies like STAPHYSAGRIA and COFFEA can also help. It is worth thinking about giving chamomile to cats who are difficult to groom either because they dislike being touched or because they find the grooming process uncomfortable as the hair is tugged.

**Bach Flower Remedies** (see p. 12 for dosage and pp. 15–16 for administration)

VINE (*Vitus vinifera*) In humans the vine state relates to people who are greedy for power and domination and have no respect for others, and will stop at nothing to get their own way. This same state can be seen in cats who terrorize the neighbourhood, and are particularly aggressive and unscrupulous. This is the sort of cat who mounts raids into enemy territory, even entering through the cat-flap and beating up the unsuspecting occupants. Vine can also be used in a household where one particular cat wants to be dominant and keeps attacking or bullying all the others. In practice it has proved to be one of the most effective and useful remedies.

BEECH (*Fagus sylvatica*) is suited to arrogant cats who are also intolerant and lack understanding. Use beech to help introduce new cats into a household where the 'pecking order' is likely to be upset. In most situations there is one existing cat who is likely to react badly, often in a very mean, violent way. Beech-type cats are strict and usually dominant types and do not readily allow anything that is a likely threat to their stability. Beech can help transform the situation.

CHICORY (*Cichorium intybus*) has a special place in treating a cat who has been upset and redirects its pent-up feelings on its owner or another cat in the same household. Situations likely to trigger this include owners going away, or furniture being moved around, or the introduction of another pet into the house. The underlying cause of all of this is a feeling of self-pity, which stems from a self-centred possessive nature and a desire to always have its own way. Chicory cats (often Burmese), not surprisingly, are over-attached to their owners and the bottom may well fall out of their world when their guardians disappear for a while.

IMPATIENS (*Impatiens glandulifera*) suits cats who are not generally nice to know. They are irritable by nature and overreact to situations swiftly and vehemently. Inwardly tense, they live life in the fast lane. They rush here and there with boundless energy, eat quickly as if there were no tomorrow and prefer for the most part to remain on their own. They do not approve of trespassers, nor of new animals introduced into the household. Although the anger flares up quickly, it is quick to pass, and all is well after a short time. Impatiens evokes feelings of patience and gentleness.

VERVAIN (*Verbena officinalis*) The competitive aspect of cat life is covered by vervain, sometimes confused with vine. Vervain-type cats are overenthusiastic and impulsive. They are conscious that they must, at all costs, keep their domain in order, and see off any intruder. In so doing these cats fanatically burn up so much nervous energy that most of this class are thin, sleek and athletic, never gaining weight no matter how much they eat. Their nature is, not surprisingly, irritable and notably so if crossed or upset by any unjust occurrence. They are sometimes akin to badly behaved hyperactive children and in the same way an additive-free diet may help.

SCLERANTHUS (*Scleranthus annuus*) helps adjust inner emotional balance and stabilises mood swings. It is useful in periods of transition where there may be a cat who accepts a new arrival one day and then is aggressive to the newcomer the next. This pattern can repeat endlessly and can prove particularly tiring for all concerned. Scleranthus is well worth trying in an effort to alleviate the problem.

---

*The name Zorro conjures up visions of a hero, eager and upstanding, defying evil and believing in all that is good. Not so Zorro, the cat who governed with a reign of terror over all the local moggies.*

As an aggressive young male cat he was trouble from the start. Even neutering made no difference to his unwarranted behaviour. He was irritable and short-tempered, hated fuss and defended his territory with an iron paw. Any cat coming near his domain was dealt with swiftly and violently. As he grew older his desire for power grew accordingly and he started raiding other people's gardens to seek out and then assault the feline inhabitants. Stunned by power he then decided that garden takeovers were not enough, so he then embarked on entering through whatever cat-flaps were open to invade the privacy of the house.

Needless to say, the owners of the local cats started to complain, not only at the increasing vets bills to patch up the unfortunate victims, but also at the fact that Zorro was consuming large quantities of food on each raid.

Zorro's owners, only too aware of the problem, decided to seek help.

Zorro's lean build, active nature, desire for warmth and general demeanour matched NUX VOMICA well, which was given in the 30th potency twice daily. After a period of two weeks he had calmed down, living life at a more sedate pace. He became more amenable and was seen to sit on a lap every now and then. Unfortunately putting a stop to his career was not quite so easy. He was still raiding neighbours' houses and assaulting the occupants, even if it was without quite the same vigour. The Bach flower remedy VINE was added for the dominant power-seeking side of his character which within a month produced spectacular results. Now a reformed character, Zorro stays within his own grounds, and only occasionally repeats his former violent behaviour. Luckily these instances are so rare that they are soon forgotten.

# Coping with an Angry Cat

Cats who feel great annoyance at some grievance, real or imagined, are a problem. There are those who are short-tempered and angry by nature (and hence difficult to cope with), and those who are normally even-tempered, but for some reason are feeling disgruntled and upset with life. There are quite a few ways of approaching the problem and many remedies to help which will need careful consideration before selecting the most appropriate.

If your cat is suddenly acting in an angry way, such as giving you a claws-out swipe for no reason, it might be worth taking it to your vet to make sure there is no underlying physical cause, such as pain from toothache, or irritation from fleas or eczema, or perhaps an infected bite from another cat. If your vet pronounces it a hundred per cent fit, than take a look at the following remedies.

**Homoeopathic Remedies** (see pp. 8–10 for dosages and pp. 15–16 for their administration)

ACONITE (Monkshood or Wolf's Bane, *Aconitum napellus*) Short-lived anger associated with fear may be suited to aconite treatment. Use it in acute situations where the emotions have been aroused and your normally happy cat turns into a terror lurking in the corner. The cat is easily startled, fears touch and seems anxious. This anxiety is translated into anger which can be very violent. The situation can sometimes arise post-operatively, and, as I have said, can be linked to pain which your cat finds difficult to tolerate.

ANACARDIUM (The Marking Nut Tree, *Anacardium orientale*) is a strange remedy which can be used where anger is associated with an undesirable, malicious nature. Anacardium-type cats are considered renegades and not often liked, particularly by the neighbours, whose own cats may well suffer as a result of a visit by the tearaway. How do you know if your cat fits the description? Well, your cat will have a poor memory and a tendency to be irritable and violent. It will feel the cold, eat and drink in a hurry, be generally thirsty and spend a disproportionate amount of time attending to its posterior. If it also suffers from a skin problem, such as rashes, which itches intolerably, then anacardium is the right choice.

AURUM (Metallic gold) type cats are given to outbursts of rage and anger especially in times of stress. They are not happy with life and may seem discontented and depressed. On sunny days they brighten up (they love sunshine) and appear miserable when it rains. They overreact to everyday situations and are particularly sensitive to noise.

CHAMOMILLA (German chamomile) Anger associated with impatience can be treated with chamomilla, along with a sensitive, irritable, spiteful, easily vexed nature. If you have a cat like this, it will not be a pleasant character to live with, by any means, as its short-temper will reveal. Your cat will not tolerate interference of any kind and will lash out for no apparent reason. It will not like a new cat in the household, and little will please it. Warn your vet that heavy gloves will be required if he *really* wants to examine your cat. Symptoms suited to chamomilla can arise after surgery and are often associated with pain, so remember its use in this context.

HEPAR SULPH. (Calcium sulphide) Cats who benefit from this treatment have a very sensitive nature and are very easily irritated, probably due to feelings of dejection and sadness. Other cats find the hepar sulph. types difficult to live with as they have a quarrelsome streak in their nature and are inordinately touchy. As with CHAMOMILLA-type cats, pain is a problem and not well tolerated. They are sensitive to cold (especially draughts), which tends to make them feel worse. Eating and warmth have a euphoric effect and can help calm the situation. This type of cat has a predisposition towards bite wounds quickly turning septic, and this should be borne in mind when selecting their remedy.

LYCOPODIUM (Club moss) Along with NUX VOMICA and CHAMOMILLA, lycopodium suits cats who are easily angered and short-tempered. Is your cat very quickly annoyed and always seems to be under stress, appearing somewhat apprehensive and sensitive? Basically, it is suffering from a lack of confidence which expresses itself through anger. It will often dwell on past events and is apt to harbour resentment. Its appetite is either very good or poor: it picks at food. Either way it is prone to be thin.

NITRICUM ACIDUM (Nitric acid) will suit cats of a vindictive, obstinate personality. If your cat is like this, it will get angry when it wants to get even and seek revenge on a rival. Problems arise of course, if your cat's attempt to square things up is thwarted by confinement to barracks or a stay at the cattery for a week or so.

NUX VOMICA (Poison nut) is one of the most frequently indicated remedies fitting those cats of a lean build, who are by nature quick, active, irritable, over-anxious and nervous. They are over-sensitive to noise, bright lights and the presence of others, taking a positive dislike to being handled for any reason and, given half the chance, will attempt an immediate escape. Quarrels with other cats are common as are outbursts of anger and rage, although they probably feel better afterwards.

STAPHYSAGRIA (Stavesacre) helps deal with anger arising from pent-up deep-seated emotions of resentment and indignation. For more about this see p. 106.

TARENTULA HISPANIA (Spanish spider) prepared from spider venom, is associated with sudden changes in mood. Your cat will respond to this, if it is inclined to be cunning and sly, and appears as a normal happy creature one moment, with a character change taking place in a matter of seconds. What you end up with is a destructive, violent angry creature who appears almost possessed.

**Bach Flower Remedies** (see p. 12 for dosages and pp. 15–16 for their administration)

IMPATIENS (*Impatiens glandulifera*) Its keynote is impatience as the name happens to suggest. This leads to irritability and tension which ultimately is expressed as anger. Characteristics of cats who are likely to benefit include both an active and energetic nature. They always appear in a hurry and rush about the house from one place to another. Although their anger is easily roused, it passes just as quickly.

VERVAIN (*Verbena officinalis*) The type of cats suited to vervain also appear energetic and are always here or there. They have little time to be a lap cat. Their overenthusiasm leads to a degree of exhaustion and irritability. The general strain may lead to the development of illness, and in the course of things temper becomes a little short.

VINE (*Vitus vinifera*) Every veterinary practice comes to hear of the sort of cat that suits vine. This cat will terrorize all neighbouring cats, providing extra work in the way of bites and other injuries. It will strive to dominate and control all the surrounding territory. It seems almost tyrannical and often has the temper to match!

**Aromatherapy** (see pp. 13–14 for methods of application)

YLANG YLANG (*Cananga odorata*) has a short-term soothing effect particularly where anger arises out of frustration or jealousy.

LAVENDER (*Lavandula officinalis*), widely used and versatile, can help soothe away unwanted emotions, such as impatience, irritability and fear and consequently calm the situation by removing feelings of anger.

CHAMOMILE (*Anthemis nobilis*) is one of the safest and most useful aromatherapy oils. It has a soothing anti-inflammatory effect and helps relieve pain-induced anger. In this context it can be used post-operatively. On the psychological side, it is well known for its calming effect in relieving tension and anxiety which are underlying causes of anger.

# *Is Your Cat Restless, Agitated, Anxious?*

A state of nervousness, seemingly on edge and never able to settle may have arisen from a fundamental distrust of people in general, or it may be from a distrust of any new situation. Is there anything in your behaviour that might have made your cat like this? Do you perhaps shout to vent your rage in private? Have you noticed if your cat is more shifty in some situations than in others? Some ca s behave like this the moment they hear the rustle of wicker, even if it is not their cat-basket and no visit to the vet is imminent. I know of one cat who will never let his mistress stand between himself and the cat-flap for fear of being scooped up into his basket and taken on a car journey. Or is there a strange cat perhaps terrorizing your neighbourhood? It is worth trying to analyse the cause before turning to these natural remedies, some of which can be quite effective.

**Herbal Remedies** (see p. 5 for dosage and p. 15–16 for administration)

Herbal remedies are often slow to act and are therefore more suitable for treating long-term problems of anxiety. Consider using VALERIAN (p. 126), SKULLCAP (p. 126), CHAMOMILE (p. 128) or HOPS (p. 126).

**Homoeopathy** (see pp. 8–10 for dosage and pp. 15–16 for administration)

ARSENICUM ALBUM (White arsenic) Cats who are suited to arsenicum treatment are fairly refined and always look neat and tidy. Yet they are restless, nervous individuals. They appear anxious and worried, often for no real reason at all. They seem to have an underlying fear of what might just happen, and other more specific fears, particularly of being alone. Symptoms tend to become more intense during the evening and then towards midnight.

General physical manifestations of this nervousness include a desire for warmth, a thirst for small frequent drinks, and a dry coat which may contain dandruff-like flakes.

ACONITE (Monkshood) In the short term, aconite, especially when used in the 1M potency, can help calm the most anxious worried animal, but it needs to be given fairly frequently. The type of cat who will respond to it is agitated, and seems unable to settle even for a moment. It may cry out as if in pain, expressing feelings of anguish and fear. It will be sensitive to the slightest noise, and become excited and uncontrollable.

LYCOPODIUM (Club moss) The anxious cat who can be treated with lycopodium differs from cats for whom ARSENICUM is suitable. Their anxiety originates in a lack of confidence, a fundamental fear of strangers and distrust of anything new. This type of cat is intelligent and active, and needs to be occupied. Its temper can be short if provoked or caught unawares. It prefers to be outside rather than shut in. It will avoid getting too warm, yet basically doesn't like the cold, as deep down they are rather chilly individuals.

RHUS TOX (Poison ivy) The cat who will respond to rhus tox feels despondent and confused, is generally suspicious, and likes to be left alone, undisturbed. Moving around, pacing up and down, eases its anxious feelings.

ARGENTUM NITRICUM (Silver nitrate) Mental anxiety in a cat, with impulsive, hurried behaviour, might well respond to this. It suits the sort of cat who always appears in a hurry and seems generally anxious, apprehensive, easily angered and excited. They are difficult animals to examine, as they will not stay still for long, and will run off if given the least chance.

KALI PHOS. (Potassium phosphate) is better suited to shy, younger cats. Their nervous energies can sometimes leave them drained. They are anxious, fearing confrontations with other cats and unfamiliar people. This state of nervous tension makes your cat jumpy, and irritable if upset.

IGNATIA (St Ignatius bean) Use ignatia to help where anxiety and restlessness result from a shock, or where grief and worry are the primary cause, most commonly after the loss of a close companion, or the death or departure of a well-loved owner.

VALERIANA (Valerian) This is valerian in its potentized homoeopathic form, rather than the direct plant extract which is often used in herbal medicine. It can be used to treat sensitive, anxious cats who are prone to become excited and uncontrollable, and makes a useful remedy for cats who do not travel well.

**Bach Flower Remedies** see p. 12 for dosage and pp. 15–16 for administration)

AGRIMONY (*Agrimonia eupatoria*) The type of cat that agrimony can help often appears normal, but in reality is riddled with anxiety and worry. Look for changes in your cat's behaviour, particularly restlessness, as the cat keeps on the move to occupy itself and take its mind off its worries. Eventually the continued agitation and underlying concern can cause physical illness. If you can spot where agrimony is needed, then you can prevent the problem progressing to this stage altogether.

ASPEN (*Populus tremula*) Cats who need aspen are vulnerable to the anxieties of everyday life. They lack the inbuilt protection that most of us take for granted. They are afraid and anxious, but not of anything in particular. Their fears are often groundless and unsubstantiated but at worst can lead to strange panic attacks and unexplained behaviour. Aspen removes these strange anxieties and results in a calmer, less nervous and better adjusted cat.

MIMULUS (*Mimulus guttatus*) Use mimulus where anxiety and restlessness are due to known fears (in contrast to aspen). Cats likely to benefit are naturally shy, timid and afraid. They react to sudden noises, run away from strangers and are overcautious. Mimulus transforms this state, increasing confidence and allowing the cat to confront its anxieties with courage.

RED CHESTNUT (*Aesculus carnea*) will suit cats who become anxious when separated from their owners and boarded in a cattery. The cats who are very close to their owners often fret and show signs of anxiety, racing round the pen, clawing at the wire and in extreme cases injuring themselves. This excessive concern for their owner leads to a state of anxiety, sometimes so bad that the cat actually injures itself in a frantic attempt to confront its feelings.

WHITE CHESTNUT (*Aesculus hippocastanum*) Persistent, everpresent worries underlie the type of anxiety that this remedy helps. Again this can be linked to owner separation and worry about the future. Rather than expressing their feelings as the red chestnut cat would, these animals pace around anxiously or become depressed and isolated, withdrawing into themselves.

ROCK ROSE (*Helianthemum nummularium*) Use rock rose in emergency situations such as accidents that create sudden, extreme states of anxiety. It can help cats who have been trapped or rescued, calming them back into more rational behaviour.

**Aromatherapy** (see pp. 13–14 for application)

CHAMOMILE (*Matricaria recutica*) has proved to be one of the most useful calming oils. Its safe soothing effects are well known and it can be used for most cases of anxiety, even in younger cats.

LAVENDER (*Lavandula angustifolia*) Anxious, restless cats can often benefit from lavender, either by massage, by vaporization or by sprinkling a few drops of neat oil around the house or on the cat's bedding. It is one of the most calming of all the aromatherapy oils.

GERANIUM (*Pelargonium graveolens*) Geranium helps allay nervous tension and anxiety, especially where linked to stress situations. It is one of the oils that helps rebalance the body when it is upset.

# Cats with the Blues

It is strange to think that cats suffer from bouts of depression, yet they do. Those that know their pets well can tell when they sometimes undergo mood changes or mood swings. Some cats are very sensitive to atmosphere and can sense upsets which can reflect on their well-being and feeling of harmony.

Cats can feel depressed when they are left on their own for too long, especially when their owners decide to go away on holiday. If cats have to go into a cattery, they can feel abandoned, and suffer anxiety from the separation. They may refuse to eat for days and sit hunched up in a corner. Cats can also feel depressed during bouts of illness. Never mistake depression for actual health problems which might cause lethargy. If in doubt consult your vet. However, before resorting to any medical treatment, try playing with your cat more, and, in general, spend more time with it. Try to stimulate its interest in its surroundings. Often a 'boring' cat reflects a boring owner, and to a certain extent a cat is responsive in direct proportion to the amount of effort its owner is prepared to make.

**Herbal Remedies** (see p. 5 for dosages and pp. 15–16 for administration)

CATNIP (Catmint, *Nepeta cataria*) provides a wonderful uplift for depressed felines, and they are undeniably attracted to it. Its dried leaves are often used to stuff toys for cats to play with, and provide hours of fun, especially when their owners join in. If you have the plant growing in your garden then bruise a few leaves and place in a bag for your cat to enjoy.

VALERIAN (*Valeriana officinalis*) is better known for its sedative properties when used medicinally, but the dried root is just as attractive to cats as catnip. Its only drawback is that some people find the aroma of valerian rather unpleasant – no doubt the reason why most cats find it irresistible.

**Homoeopathic Remedies** (see pp. 8–10 for dosages and pp. 15-16 for administration)

CALCIUM CARBONATE (from an oyster shell) suits overweight, lazy, lethargic cats, the ones who are slow and dull and totally uninteresting. Everything is an effort for them and they would rather find a warm cosy spot away from it all to just curl up and go to sleep. Even going outdoors is too much to cope with, particularly if it's cold. They dislike being alone, yet fear strangers, because this sort of cat is basically timid and shy. They are sensitive to noise and jumpy. They are unable to digest milk and are prone to bouts of diarrhoea.

SEPIA (Ink of the cuttlefish) is more suited to females than males, and can often help where depression is due to indifference. The underlying problem is that the cat is worn out. Its muscles lack tone and moving around is an effort. It often prefers to be on its own, and attempts at comforting are not welcomed. Warm places are sought and cold aggravates its black moods. Skin problems, particularly loss of hair over the back and down the legs, are sometimes a symptom.

LACHESIS (Bushmaster snake venom), like SEPIA, is more suited to female cats than males. Mornings are not the best times for the lachesis-type cat, as they wake up feeling sad, depressed and moody. They are usually of a suspicious nature and somewhat anxious and restless. Undue handling is not appreciated. Particularly sensitive areas include around the throat and stomach. Lachesis cats are usually very vocal and will let you know at full volume if they are feeling in the least displeased.

LILIUM TIGRINUM (Tiger lily) Where depression is profound and where sympathy and interference are resented, the cat may benefit from this remedy. Your cat will most likely be an unpleasant character who hisses and scratches. There is often a wild look in its eyes and a tendency to move about in a hurry. Your cat will not be suffering from loss of appetite but may show excessive thirst.

**Bach Flower Remedies** (see p. 12 for dosages and pp. 15–16 for administration)

WILD ROSE (*Rosa canina*) Some cats appear to be totally boring, and are no fun to own. They never seem to want to play and show little or no interest in life in general. Their underlying problem is sadness and feelings associated with unhappiness. In fact they have almost given up and resigned themselves to an indifferent existence. As well as playing with them, give them wild rose which will revitalize them and help them see life in a new light.

GENTIAN (*Gentianella amarella*) Some cats are easily depressed by life's events. Their outlook is pessimistic; worry, and suffering feelings of inadequacy and dejection. They are easily discouraged and are often picked upon by other cats, becoming downtrodden and sullen.

A transformation can follow the use of gentian. They learn to cope with conflicts and will develop more self-confidence. They see hope and that life's problems are not insurmountable. Think of using gentian where there are changes in circumstance, such as moving house, loss of a companion animal or during illness where recovery is not so fast as expected.

MUSTARD (*Sinapis arvensis*) Useful where there are definite bouts of depression, in between periods of normality. There is no underlying reason for the changes in mood (compared with gentian) and where gloom strikes, you are left with a sad and melancholic character who will go out of its way to make sure its feelings are known to all.

SWEET CHESTNUT (*Castanea sativa*) can help with feelings of helplessness, abandonment and despair. It is sometimes worth giving to cats who become depressed when left by their owners in boarding catteries. Siamese or Burmese are often like this and suffer from separation anxiety. They will refuse to eat and sit gloomily in the corner of a boarding pen refusing to move. Occasionally quite the opposite happens and there is frantic, near-manic behaviour with the cat throwing itself around the pen in a state of absolute despair and helplessness.

**Aromatherapy** (see pp. 13–14 for application)

ROSEMARY (*Rosmarinus officinalis*) oil is a stimulant which will help rejuvenate a depressed cat, especially one which seems lethargic without any particular cause. Rosemary will provide both mental and physical stimulation.

CLARY SAGE (*Salvia sclarea*) (which is different from the common garden sage) is one of the most widely used oils in treating human depression, and it seems to work on cats as well. It induces feelings of euphoria and calmness. Where muscles are tense it will relax the animal at the same time.

LAVENDER (*Lavandula officinalis*) is the most commonly used of oils and very safe. Like the others it can be used to help cats who are feeling low. It boosts the immune system and can help with post-illness recovery.

YLANG YLANG (*Cananga odorata*) is another euphoric oil which can lift depressive moods. Try ylang ylang where your cat appears angry, frustrated or lacking in confidence.

# Mopers

Cats do sometimes tend to give up, when they are ill or become depressed, slowing down the healing process and reducing their chances of making a speedy or full recovery.

> *Tollo was an eighteen-month-old neutered ginger-and-white male with a real zest for life. His energetic, inquisitive nature eventually landed him in trouble when he leapt from a shed roof and miscalculated his descent, colliding with a dustbin and breaking his front right leg. The local vet x-rayed his leg and found that Tollo had neatly fractured both his radius and ulna.*
>
> *A plaster cast was applied and all was well until he was sent home the next day. As the cast was curbing his style, Tollo set about dismantling the vet's work. In a little under twenty minutes the cast lay in shreds, and, feeling pleased that he was now free of his burden, Tollo limped along in front of his owners, calling jubilantly. Another stay at the vet's and Tollo returned home, not only with another plaster cast, but also wearing the latest in Elizabethan collars designed to prevent him from attacking it. As if this was not enough, he was indignantly confined to one room of the house to stop him charging about and waving the clumsy appendage around.*
>
> (cont.)

(cont.)

*In fact the collar worked extremely well but made Tollo feel incredibly miserable: he would spend all day moping around with virtually no interest in life. Two weeks of this and he was taken back to the surgery to have the cast changed. Home once more and confined to barracks, Tollo's demeanour did not improve. Another two weeks and another cast change which revealed that the fracture had not yet started to heal. This was thought strange for a young cat, since fractures in young animals normally heal very quickly.*

*After a further two weeks of treatment, an X-ray revealed that the fracture had barely started to knit together. Tollo's slow progress appeared due to his lack of vitality and general apathy.*

Think of using the remedies below for cats who are hospitalized, or for those who are for one reason or another incapacitated (by a plaster cast like Tollo for example) or seem to be suffering from the after-effects of treatment, drug or otherwise. These remedies can also help in adverse situations where circumstances change, and make their life difficult, with undue stress on an animal.

**Homoeopathic Remedy** (see pp. 8–10 for dosages, and pp. 15–16 for administration)

ARSENICUM ALBUM (White arsenic) has many applications, including assisting recovery (whatever the illness): it can remove feelings of despair and hopelessness, and, at the same time, provide support for the body. At times it can literally be a life-saver, even to cats at death's door when all hope is past. When recovery is no longer possible, arsenicum can provide a calming ambience in the last moments of life.

**Bach Flower Remedies** (see p. 12 for dosages and pp. 15–16 for administration)

GORSE (*Ulex europaeus*) relates to hope and really can benefit animals who seem to have given up, often those suffering chronic health problems with little hope of full recovery. Many treatments may have been tried but nothing seems to work that well. In part this may be psychological and linked to inbuilt feelings of despondency and despair of recovery. Underlying this there is an inner hope and occasional periods of happiness which gorse can build upon. Gorse strengthens inherent healing powers and combats the negative state of mind that aids the progress of illness.

OAK (*Quercus robur*) Cats for which oak is suitable are normally strong-willed and some of life's survivors. They have strong personalities but can be brought down by illness or other overwhelming odds. They put up a brave fight against disease or other adversity but ultimately are unable to struggle on, as their resources are drained and they become exhausted. They never quite give up though, even in the face of great adversity. Oak reinforces this resolve, increasing strength and courage.

CRAB APPLE (*Malus pumila*) helps purify the system on both a mental and physical level. Its greatest use is after illness to help detoxify the system of drugs, anaesthetics and like substances which can have an almost overpowering influence on well-being. Although crab apple can be used to treat any cat, where the ill-effects of medication are thought to be causing problems (such as dullness and depression), it works very well in those cats who are normally fastidiously tidy and neat, and demand order in their lives.

OLIVE (*Olea europoea*) replenishes energy when the system has been drained by a period of strain. Think about using olive after a long illness when all reserves have gone into healing, or following a period of intense worry where mental resources have been drained completely. A cat trapped in a garage or shed for several days on end, desperately trying to get out and finally released in a run-down state, energy reserves depleted, would benefit from olive.

*In the case of Tollo, mentioned on pp. 45–6, he was treated with a combination of GORSE and OAK for despondency, together with the homoeopathic remedy SYMPHYTUM (comfrey) to encourage the fracture to heal. Within four days Tollo was back to his former self, leaping around, eating better and demanding attention once more and desperately trying to get up to his usual antics. Two and a half weeks later the fracture was perfectly healed.*

# Demon Rippers and Scratchers

Has your sofa been ripped apart, furniture legs scraped, or holes scratched out of your carpet? There is a distinction to be made between what is 'normal' scratching behaviour and what is abnormal and requiring treatment.

Scratching is an essential part of feline behaviour, helping to keep claws in good working order. For this purpose your cat will select one or two sites within the house, which, from your viewpoint may not be the best, but are usually considered the finest a cat can lay his paws on. Providing a more suitable alternative such as a scratching post, in close proximity to the piece of furniture in question will often solve the problem.

Where there are multiple scratching sites, as opposed to the normal one or two, then you have a problem. By marking so many areas the cat is leaving a visual message (as well as leaving scent), marking out its territory. The underlying reasons here are the same as for indoor sprayers – to improve confidence and sense of security, see under SPRAYING pp. 117–22. In fact treat such cats in the same way recommended for sprayers, using some of the same remedies, namely the homoeopathic remedy STAPHYSAGRIA or the Bach flower remedies WILLOW, WALNUT, CHICORY, LARCH or MIMULUS.

# Feline Fears and Phobias

A cat's mind is more complex than you might imagine and subject to a whole array of psychological problems. Domestic cats suffer from some of the same conditions as people, such as apprehension, agoraphobia, claustrophobia, fear of crowds, of travel, thunder. Needless to say this can make life for the affected feline somewhat difficult and sometimes presents practical problems for owners.

Problems may start at an early age. Young kittens are normally exposed to the general hustle and bustle of daily life, kittens learn from it: how to cope with and adjust to normal events, such as startling noises, the sudden appearance of other animals and unfamiliar humans. It is a learning process for which they rely on their mothers. Some unfortunate kittens may find themselves with inexperienced mothers, whilst others just fail to learn properly what is normal and what is not. For a few there is inadequate exposure to the stimuli that they would naturally encounter (and normally duly cope with) in the course of adult life.

Where adult cats are concerned, sudden and alarming experiences (for which they may not be prepared) can cause loss of confidence and leave the cat feeling shattered. Some cats will get over such events quickly and return to normal life again. Others will suffer the psychological consequences and develop specific or non-specific fears and phobias. In many cases this is an extension of the natural built-in mechanism for survival which may be working overtime to the cat's detriment.

For whatever reason, an ill-prepared kitten or an apprehensive adult will suffer a higher level of anxiety, insecurity and unease. This may express itself as a timid shy creature who hides away and stalks around, crouching low and dashing from place to place hoping not to be seen. Or it may express itself in aggression: a cat may respond to anxiety by biting or scratching to cover up its inadequacies. Treatment with natural remedies can often help, providing a solution to complex problems that would otherwise be quite difficult to treat.

## NON-SPECIFIC GENERAL FEARS

**Homoeopathic Remedies** (see pp. 8–10 for dosage and pp. 15–16 for administration)

ACONITE (Monkshood) is a short-acting remedy for general use in acute situations after trauma or fright, where there is fear and anxiety with a general sense of foreboding. The cat may be restless; it may also not want to be touched and would rather hide away. High potencies such as 1M work best.

ARGENTUM NITRICUM (Silver nitrate) There is a certain type of cat who responds well to argentum nitricum (see p. 37, [ANXIETY 2]). Stress may also cause physical symptoms such as urination and diarrhoea at inopportune moments when the cat feels worried. Fear may be such that your cat trembles. Company and reassurance are very important.

GELSEMIUM (Yellow jasmine) In complete contrast to the cat who responds to ARGENTUM, this type of cat is timid, and is rooted to the spot when worried, rather than rushing away. Fear produces a sense of paralysis and weakness. They would rather be alone and hide away than confront the problem face to face. Vets know this type of cat too well. When hospitalized they invariably hide under the bedding pretending not to be seen. This is also the sort of cat who clings ardently to its owner in the consulting room, claws dug in well in an attempt to avoid examination. This is all done to reduce stress to which they are prone, and which produces, on occasion, worried excitement and fear-induced diarrhoea.

PHOSPHORUS (The element) Affection and attention is uppermost in the mind of the cat who responds to phosphorus well. Those are lap cats who take every single opportunity to follow their owner around the house and demand fuss at every conceivable opportunity. They are, however, extremely sensitive and easily startled by such things as sudden noises and bangs. Cats who respond to phosphorus usually tend to be thirsty and dislike being left alone.

CAUSTICUM (Potassium hydrate) Older cats often respond well to causticum. They tend to be rather sad and feel particularly worried at night when alone. Other concurrent symptoms may also respond at the same time, particularly rheumatic stiffness which is worse when the weather is clear and fine and better in damp wet conditions.

LYCOPODIUM (Club moss) The type of cat responding well to this has been described on p. 36. Company, whether it is another cat or human, makes the situation better by boosting its sense of security. Timidity, occasionally seen as aggression, is also a common feature. This type of cat is usually lean; its appetite is either excessive or fussy.

CALC. CARB. (Calcium carbonate) The cat who responds to calc. carb. is a little on the plump side and somewhat lazy. It has a degree of obstinacy, forgetfulness and apprehension, coupled with an anxious nature which manifests as a general state of fearfulness. Fears are most felt in the evening, rather than the daytime. So if this is when your normally inactive over-weight cat starts to act strangely, think about trying this remedy.

GRAPHITES (Black lead, Plumbago) This type of cat also tends to be a little overweight and on the lazy side. They are likely to be timid and shy and consequently easily worried, upset and readily frightened. They take a despondent view of life and are naturally cautious and hesitant.

IGNATIA (St Ignatius bean) is a remedy more suited to female rather than male cats. They are easily frightened, especially by noise. Their general nature is often one of sadness with an inclination to brood over past events and worry, bottling up their feelings. Timidity and fearfulness are evident and they are often hurried in their movements. Sudden changes of mood are sometimes apparent.

SEPIA (Ink of the cuttlefish) See p. 41 for cats who respond well to sepia. They are not terribly brave, being of a timorous nature and subject to a range of non-specific fears.

**Bach Flower Remedies** (see p. 12 for dosage and pp. 15–16 for administration)

ROCK ROSE (*Helianthemum nummularium*) & RESCUE REMEDY Always administer rock rose or Rescue Remedy following any injury which causes distress, or after a near-miss with a car. It can even be used to calm cats before a trip in the cat basket or a car journey, especially if they find such occasions har-rowing. Rock rose is one of the five remedies included in Rescue Remedy but can equally be used alone where called for. Rock Rose can be used after any crisis situation where fear is obviously acute. Such times are usually short-lasting but often very distressing for cat and owner. The extent of the fear may cause urination or defecation, or aggressive outbursts. It is not unknown for cats to escape their owner's clutches and race around in a maniacal fashion, avoiding capture.

ASPEN (*Populus tremula*) While ROCK ROSE is used for acute situations, think of using aspen for more general anxiety situations. It suits more nervous cats who are apprehensive and outwardly fearful but not of anything specific: they just seem worried by life. They are wary, fearful that something is going to happen. On occasion they may panic for no obvious reason, others will hide away and avoid company. It is a good remedy to give pre-operatively to anxious animals and reduces stress levels all round!

## Aromatherapy (see pp. 13–14 for application)

All of these oils can be used diluted in a carrier oil for massage. Many cats will appreciate the extra attention that massage affords, not to mention the beneficial effects from the oils. Being realistic, there will be situations where this is not at all practical for obvious reasons. At such times the oils can be used in an electric vaporizer placed in the same room as the cat. Remember to carefully place it in a safe place where it cannot get knocked over.

LAVENDER (*Lavandula officinalis*) Essential oil of lavender has many many applications, one of which is helping deal with fear and fright. Gentle massage with lavender is remarkably soothing and calming and where wounds are also present, will also encourage healing. This versatile oil has analgesic and anti-microbial properties which make it ideal for first-aid situations.

FRANKINCENSE (*Boswellia carteri*) This oil has a warm, almost spicy scent. It can be used in situations of panic and terror even when a cause is not identifiable. Gentle massage can induce feelings of security, reduce irritability and lift apprehension.

ROSE (*Rosa centifolia*) Rose induces a feeling of well-being and relieves anxiety. Use it in times of crisis where feelings of terror and panic abound. It can help in stressful situations generally.

## SPECIFIC FEARS

When your cat shows a specific fear – of strange children perhaps or travelling in a car – there are two schools of thought. One, that you should protect your cat entirely from the source of the fear – which will certainly help in the short term; the other, that you should expose your cat to the source of its fear, first of all in very short sessions, and gradually increase them, simultaneously reassuring your cat, and rewarding it at the end of each session with a special titbit. Some remedies do exist with distinct uses in treating some of the more common feline psychological problems. Basic pointers to their use are included where necessary in the following sections. Remember though that natural remedies alone will not always solve your problems, and you should first always look to see whether you can reduce the cat's fear by modifying your own behaviour or habits, where particular fears are concerned.

**Bach Flower Remedies** (see p. 12 for dosage and pp. 15–16 for administration)

MIMULUS (*Mimulus guttatus*) is one of the most useful remedies for dealing with definite fears and phobias. The keynote for mimulus is fear of known things, which contrasts to aspen where the fears are non-specific. This could be any sort of fear. Fear of closed spaces, of a certain person or animal, fear of being hurt. Cats who respond well are often very cautious by nature, unsure of themselves and sensitive to changes in their environment.


## MY CAT HATES BEING TOUCHED OR APPROACHED

Except for ferals, few cats are unapproachable. If, however, you do own a cat who does not want to be handled under any circumstances, then you have a problem.

Try the behavioural approach first. Possibly it was never handled as a kitten, or it had a very bad experience with a human, when very young. Frightened cats don't like direct confrontation. Never grab at it. Hold a special titbit in your hand and make encouraging noises, but don't move towards it, or look at it directly in the eye. If you do have to look directly, be disarming and blink a lot. Wait for the cat to come to you. Try this a little every day. You will probably need endless patience, but you may eventually be rewarded. It certainly works with feral cats. Many mellow with age as they gain confidence.

The following remedies may also help.

**Homoeopathic Remedies** (see pp. 8–10 for dosages and pp. 15–16 for administration)

HYOSCYAMUS (Henbane, *Hyoscyamus niger*) This is an important homoeopathic remedy and is one of the most valuable in treating ferals. Fear is very dominant, expressed by almost maniacal behaviour or rage, that is expressed in biting and scratching. The eyes may appear red and angry and the pupils dilated. Movements are rapid and appear clumsy with the cat running into or throwing itself at the side of a pen or basket in an effort to escape. Vocal protests accompany this alarming behaviour.

HYDROPHOBINUM (Lyssin, potentized rabies virus) has been successfully used to treat feral cats when first caught and penned. It calms maniacal behaviour brought on by extreme fear and terror. This state of mind induces reckless, almost convulsive movements making the cat unapproachable and unmanageable. Salivation is common with the cat dribbling thick viscid saliva during violent rampages around the cage. Fear of water is an associated symptom seen occasionally.

LYCOPODIUM (Club moss) is not particularly suited to ferals, but more to domestic cats who become attached to one specific person and will not let any others approach or make a fuss of them. These cats are clever – real intellectuals – who feel themselves superior to all around. They are self-conscious and keep themselves to themselves, that is except for the privileged person who is allowed to pick them up and pour out a little affection. They like to have someone around, although they avoid anyone who appears unfamiliar. Temper can be short and they can become aggressive if pushed too far. Underlying many of these problems is a basic lack of self-confidence which the remedy can help redress.

NATRUM CARB. (Sodium carbonate) is indicated where there is dislike and fear of one distinct person. Although normally happy cats, they are slow to learn and not the most intelligent.

RHUS TOX (Poison ivy) is commonly associated with the treatment of arthritis and rheumatism where restlessness is a feature. The cat tends to move about, unable to settle, and is mentally agitated. Its ill-humour is coupled with a fear of unfamiliar people.

BARYTA CARB. (Barium carbonate) Cats who respond to this share a common problem with those who respond to lycopodium: lack of confidence in themselves. They are somewhat timid and wary of strangers as they are not terribly brave. This remedy works best in younger animals.

## Bach Flower Remedies

IMPATIENS is one remedy that might help, as it releases inner tension and inspires gentleness, tolerance and patience. Others suitable for ferals are:

RESCUE REMEDY which can be administered in food or water prior to capture or transportation; ROCK ROSE in particular will help allay the fear and terror feral cats suffer at such times; and CHERRY PLUM deals with the irrational scrambled thoughts that must race through the cat's mind at times like this.

In the later stages, during re-homing, think about using WILLOW to deal with the resentment and indignation surrounding capture and imprisonment. WALNUT too can help with adjustment to the new surroundings and help the cat accept what has taken place.

But some cats just hate strangers touching them, and that

---

*When younger, Prudence was mistreated and was in a very poor state when rescued at a little under seven months old. Within a few days she was neutered, then rehomed with a young couple.*

*Let loose in her new surroundings, she immediately hid herself away. Her favourite refuge was behind a wardrobe from which she would not venture out for any reason. After three days, worried that she would become ill through not eating or drinking, her new owners made attempts to entice her out which only resulted in sheer terror and panic, ultimately making things worse.*

*Essential oils of LAVENDER and ROSE were used on an electric vaporizer to provide a calming, anxiety-relieving atmosphere. This proved to be a turning point and within twenty-four hours Prudence ventured out at night to feed, drink and use the litter tray. Despite this brave move, she would still panic at the sight of any human approach, escaping once more to her safe haven.*

*For panic and terror ROCK ROSE was added to her drinking water. Unfortunately she detected this and would not drink. She did, however, take the remedy in food; this proved successful and increased her confidence generally, such that she would venture out briefly when the owners quietly called her.*

*ROCK ROSE was replaced with ASPEN for non-specific apprehensiveness and MIMULUS for her specific fears, shyness and timidity. A few weeks later she was a different cat and would allow herself to be picked up and stroked. Further assurance was provided at these opportunities by massage using LAVENDER to relax her and YLANG YLANG to boost her confidence in herself. In the space of just six weeks Prudence was transformed from an unapproachable cat to the most affectionate and happy feline any owner could wish to have.*

often includes the unfortunate vet. This sort of cat can only be examined at a distance and will badly scratch or bite. Most vets are familiar with such characters. The patient either stays firmly shut in his or her basket or is manhandled using the thickest of gloves. Some cats, as their owners will dutifully explain, are in fact perfectly all right at home and only put up their defences when taken out of their customary surroundings, usually under protest. Putting on such an affront is certainly one way of avoiding the indignity of having your temperature taken! The ploy works nearly every time; perhaps they are more intelligent than we realize? The reaction is solely fear-induced and Bach's Flower Remedies, such as ROCK ROSE or RESCUE REMEDY, are worth trying.

**Homoeopathic Remedies** (see pp. 8–10 for dosages, pp. 15–16 for administration)

ARNICA (Leopard's bane) is not only suitable for accidents and injuries, but a remedy in its own right as well. Use arnica in any situation, accident or otherwise, where your cat shows a great fear of being touched or approached, and wants, at all costs, to be left alone. Even vague attempts at being kind are met with hisses, snarls and spitting and an air of agitation.

Poisonous plants often make good homoeopathic remedies with a wide variety of applications. BELLADONNA (Deadly nightshade) helps where there is a great deal of restlessness and anguish, where a cat is agitated and excitable and in a state of fright and tension almost approaching delirium. Approaches are greeted with suspicion and enthusiastic hissing and lashing out of paws. To say the least an angry cat!

STRAMONIUM (see p. 70), LYCOPODIUM (apprehensive and lacking confidence) and IGNATIA have also been of use in dealing with this problem when correctly prescribed.

## MY CAT IS TERRIFIED OF CAT SHOWS

Well-seasoned show cats take the hustle and bustle of the show scene in their stride with no qualms, and indeed there are cats who really enjoy showing off. But cat shows are unnatural settings; the cat is out of its normal territory, among the strange smells of strange cats, with people milling about, peering at them, isolated in their cages, all under strong lighting. Small wonder that the novice show cat or more nervous cat finds the whole ordeal nerve-racking. For this type of cat the event can turn into a terrifying experience with dire consequences. For some cats, anxiety will heighten their senses, and owners must be on their guard against their cat 'doing a runner'.

Many owners find that of the Bach's flower remedies, once again RESCUE REMEDY, ASPEN or MIMULUS can work very well.

**Homoeopathic Remedies** (see pp. 8–10 for dosage and pp. 15–16 for administration)

ACONITE (Monkshood, Wolf's Bane) Higher potencies work best and give good results when given the night before a show, the morning of the show and just before arriving at the event. It calms agitated and worried animals, even those which are tempted to become bad-tempered and angry.

ARGENTUM NITRICUM (Silver nitrate) suits anxious impulsive cats, whose anxiety may bring on a bout of diarrhoea or nervous urination. Senses are heightened and your cat is likely to escape if given the opportunity.

GELSEMIUM (Yellow jasmine) patients may be cowards at heart and feel fearful and unsettled by goings-on around them. Again there may be nervous urination or defecation, but their fear is usually translated into a state of stupor where the cat is so worried that it crouches down petrified and unable to move.

Cats who respond to LYCOPODIUM (Club moss) have an inherent inability to cope with changes and new experiences. For this reason this remedy is useful in young cats who appear to be apprehensive and lacking in self-confidence.

Weaker cats often are SILICEA (Silica, pure flint) types. They lack fibre, both physically and mentally. They are apt to be restless, anxious, agitated and are frightened of sudden noises which may cause excitement. Although occasionally prone to anger they are more usually submissive and cower through fear. They need desperately to be warm, as they are chilly individuals.

## MY CAT LOATHES THE CAT BASKET

Being bundled into the cat basket implies travel, which in turn implies moving the cat out of its territory, the vibration of a car in motion, and also being in a confined space for a length of time. And what is at the end of this? Usually something nasty: the vet's, a cattery, a cat show? I know cats who, at the tiniest sound of wicker being touched, are out through the catflap and over the garden wall before you can say 'whiskers'.

If you have to travel with your cat for any length of time, try putting an old coat of yours over the basket. The darkness usually reassures it and it will probably fall asleep, rather than look agitatedly out of the window at the ever-changing land-scape, which it can find very alarming (see also under STRESS pp. 125–32). But if your cat seems to be suffering more from the claustrophobic aspect than from the change of territory, then try the following.

From Bach's flower remedies, use ROCK ROSE or RESCUE REMEDY. These will normally help those cats who exhibit sheer terror and act in a maniacal way.

**Homoeopathic Remedies** (see pp. 8–10 for dosage and pp. 15–16 for administration)

You will have already encountered the homoeopathic remedy

ARGENTUM NITRICUM (Silver nitrate) elsewhere. Mental anxiety linked to an impetuous nature characterize the cat who will benefit from it. Movements are impulsive and hurried and one of its worst experiences is to be shut in a cat basket. Worse still is being shut in and unable to see out.

The uncertainty of a trip in an unfamiliar basket worries the apprehensive LYCOPODIUM (Club moss) type of cat. Repeated attempts at trying to fit an ill-humoured cat into a basket, seemingly too small, can bring out the worst aspects of the obstinate lycopodium personality.

The affectionate, gregarious cat who probably feels hurt when shut inside a basket will benefit from PULSATILLA (Wind flower). They love company and not the inside of cat baskets!

The more unusual remedy of SUCCINUM (Electron, Amber, Fossil resin) is a specific for fear of enclosed spaces that can induce a state of hysteria, cause violent vomiting or bring on asthmatic-like attacks.


## MY CAT CAN'T BEAR BEING LEFT ALONE

Some cats learn to rely totally on their owners for both physical and mental support, and can become overdependent or overattached. Such bonding problems can arise in kittens which are hand-reared, or adults who do not learn how to deal with everyday life. In some instances difficulties arise when cats have been ill and have had periods of intensive nursing care, and total owner/nurse attention for some weeks.

The crunch comes when their minders are no longer around for whatever reason. Behavioural problems can appear, originating from an underlying feeling of insecurity. Some cats will resort to destructive behaviour, some start spraying and others will become agitated and angry or just sulk.

Any solution must incorporate sensible behavioural advice involving a gradual reduction in owner dependence. The idea behind this is to lessen the cat's attachment slowly, by becoming less available, or to spread affection amongst a number of people so that the cat does not become overreliant on any one person. Natural remedies have an important part to play of course.

Useful Bach flower remedies include MIMULUS and ASPEN to cope with the actual aspect of fear of being left, and CHICORY or HEATHER to help treat those cats who are completely owner-dependent in a selfish or self-centred way. This type of cat cannot bear to be left behind and may feel angry if it is 'left out'. Chicory or heather may remove these feelings gradually, replacing them with feelings of security, protection strength and confidence. Don't forget that LARCH can be used to boost confidence particularly in kittens.

**Homoeopathic Remedies** (see pp. 8–10 for dosage and pp. 15–16 for administration)

ARSENICUM ALBUM (White arsenic) heads the list of homoeopathic remedies in this particular area. Cats suited to this remedy are fastidiously tidy, often of thin lean build and may have areas of dry scales in their coat. Temper is often short and their nature, besides being on the nervous, restless side, is sometimes not very forgiving. One of their greatest fears is of being alone without company or companionship. This may ultimately cause some cats to hide away.

For cats who show more anger together with jealousy and a propensity to make a lot of noise about things HYOSCYAMUS (Henbane) may be the solution. Yet this angry type of cat, with teeth and claws at the ready, has an underlying sense of uncertainty about life.

The type of cat very easily startled and quite likely to be irritable, especially if caught unawares will benefit from KALI

CARB. (Potassium carbonate). Unusually they like company but are not overkeen on sympathy or undue attention.

Sensitive cats can be types suited to LYCOPODIUM (Club moss); they particularly dislike being left alone. They lack confidence and tend to be apprehensive and unsure of anything new. Appetite can vary. Sometimes they are ravenously hungry yet never seem to gain weight. Alternatively they can be picky and difficult to please. Burmese cats often match to lycopodium quite well.

Cats which match PHOSPHORUS (the element) crave affection and attention and have a loving nature. They feel uneasy when left alone and feel more secure in company. Their sensitive nature means that they are unduly worried by sudden noises such as bangs or gun shots.

PULSATILLA (Wind flower) suits mainly females of a gentle yielding, good-natured disposition. They are shy and not so forward as those cats matching phosphorus. Fatty foods cause digestive problems and most pulsatilla-type cats drink very little. Anxious feelings arise in the evening and company is sought for comfort.

## MY CAT IS TOO FRIGHTENED TO GO OUT OF DOORS

Genuine fear of open spaces is fortunately extremely rare in cats. There are some kittens which do not become accustomed to going outside. Most are keen to explore at an early age and are soon happy to wander around inside the house. But until their vaccination courses are complete, they should not go outside. When they do, a whole new world awaits. Most adapt naturally, a few find the experience daunting.

Bach flower remedies can be extremely useful for helping kittens. MIMULUS (typically shy and timid), LARCH (lack of confidence) and ASPEN (generally apprehensive) have proved valuable. If necessary they can be combined together.

Adult cats can develop 'agoraphobia'. This stems from some frightening experience outside which remains in the cat's mind and is a good enough reason for staying safe inside. Road accidents, frightening encounters with dogs or aggressive cats, and violent conflicts are common causes.

In the acute situation try homoeopathic ACONITE or Bach Flower RESCUE REMEDY. Rescue remedy contains STAR OF BETHLEHEM which is the particular ingredient that helps deal with the after-effects of frightening experiences.

In longer-term treatment of agoraphobia, MIMULUS is almost certain to help some cats and it is likely that WHITE CHESTNUT could also be of use in some instances (where they are worried over a past event).

**Homoeopathic Remedies** (see pp. 8–10 for dosage and pp. 15–16 for administration)

Homoeopathically GELSEMIUM (Yellow jasmine) is the remedy of choice. General feelings of apprehension abound, with fear of what might happen, which means that the cat would rather hide away inside.

There are a few other remedies which may also be of use, namely ARGENTUM NITRICUM (Silver nitrate) suited to anxious and impulsive cats, CALC. CARB. (Calcium carbonate) which matches to sluggish but easily frightened cats and KALI PHOS. (Potassium phosphate) suited to cats which show signs of apprehension, nervousness and lack of energy, tiring easily.

**FEAR INDUCED BY PAIN**

When a cat is in pain after surgery, or unfortunately after an accident, you may find them reacting in a strange way. Many cats appear to believe that the pain is being inflicted on them from some outside source (sometimes including you) and will try to run away from it, or whoever they think is inflicting the pain. They need very gentle love in such circumstances; sometimes it is better to leave them alone in a warm and comfortable dark place, where they will feel quite unthreatened.

Excitable, sensitive cats can respond well to the homoeopathic remedy of COFFEA (Unroasted coffee), particularly those who suffer from nervous agitation and restlessness. It has a special area of use in cats who are normally calm but pain has caused unrest, anxiety and fear. Try using coffea on cats who behave irrationally and out of character after surgery.

## FEAR DURING KITTENING

Some queens do become agitated during kittening and in the stages leading up to the event. Younger, less experienced cats are more likely to feel worried, especially if there is a lot of commotion going on around. The Bach's flower RESCUE REMEDY works well in calming the situation. The homoeopathic remedy, ACONITE, can also be very effective.

## MY CAT WILL CLIMB TREES AND THEN IS TOO SCARED TO COME DOWN

Most of us have seen surefooted cats scaling the most precarious heights and jumping with ease across great voids between buildings, walls and fences. A few feel less carefree once their feet are off the ground and are less adept at mountaineering than should be the case. For those who are incompetent climbers and who may well suffer from vertigo, then help is at hand.

Bach flower remedies can help (beforehand, of course!).

MIMULUS (fear of known things and timidity), LARCH (for lack of confidence) and ASPEN (for apprehension).

**Homoeopathic Remedies** (see pp. 8–10 for dosage and pp. 15–16 for administration)

BORAX (Sodium borate) is one of the effective remedies to help cats who have trouble negotiating heights. For those for whom borax is effective, height is not really the problem, rather it is the fear of falling which induces anxiety feelings. Borax suits cats of a more generally nervous nature.

Courage is rather lacking where CUPRUM (Copper) is called for and high places induce feelings of vertigo and fear of falling.

GELSEMIUM (Yellow jasmine) will suit the timid type of cat who has a fear of falling. They would prefer to hide away and when feeling irritable would rather be left alone. At times they need support and company and in stressful situations cling closely to their owners for fear of falling and for security.

Cats who will profit from SANICULA (Water from Sanicula Springs, Ottawa, Ill, USA) have a fear of downward motion and fear of falling. They may have scaly dry areas in their coat or regions of sticky weeping dermatitis. Car sickness may also be a feature.

## MY CAT IS SCARED OF THUNDER AND SUDDEN NOISES

Almost all animals are frightened by thunder and will go to hide in a dark corner. Try to give them reassurance. Many people however, complain that their cats are terrified by any sudden noise. This may be nothing more than a bang or a loud thump, ranging from a car back-firing, gun-shots, to the doorbell. The result is a petrified, terror-stricken cat who hides away in the least accessible place and refuses to come out.

Apart from the familiar array of Bach's flower remedies, the following homoeopathic remedies can work very effectively.

**Homoeopathic Remedies** (see pp. 8–10 for dosage and pp. 15–16 for administration)

Playful friendly cats are often PHOSPHORUS (the element) types. They love affection and attention. In keeping with their perceptive reactive nature, their senses work overtime, making them extremely sensitive to all that goes on around them. Fear of thunder is common, but there is marked sensitivity to all other noises as well.

Nervous cats that are really terrified by storms nearly always benefit from RHODODENDRON (Yellow snow rose). Fear of thunder is most marked, causing extreme fear and agitation.

Where rhododendron is suited to a marked fear of thunder, BORAX (Sodium borate) can be prescribed for nervous cats which are very easily frightened. They are absolutely terrified by sudden noises such as the sound of a gun going off, even if the sound is some way off. Needless to say they are usually frightened of thunder as well.

Cats who respond to SEPIA (Ink of the cuttlefish) are more likely to be female than male. They are somewhat sad and melancholic, and apt to appear lazy rather than outwardly active. At times they can be grumpy, though they dislike being alone. Their nervous nature means that they are sensitive to the least noise including thunder.

In a real contrast to the phosphorus-type cat, the NAT. MUR. (Sodium chloride, common salt) personality dislikes fuss and attention. They would rather be left alone and not interfered with. They demand fuss only when they want it and not when you might think fit. Their senses are very acute, with sensitivity to noise a particular feature, which may cause them to panic. They are usually thirsty and quite like to eat salty foods such as fish.

## MY CAT IS PETRIFIED OF BRIGHT OR SHINING OBJECTS

This phobia is rare, but does occasionally occur. Some cats start acting strangely when they see sparkling shiny objects. There are a few recorded instances where this phenomenon has in fact induced epilepsy. The Bach flower remedy most likely to help is MIMULUS.

**Homoeopathic Remedies** (see pp. 8–10 for dosage and pp. 15–16 for administration)

STRAMONIUM (Thorn-apple) is a member of the same plant family as belladonna and shares some of its traits. Cats who respond well to it have a propensity to be irritable, short-tempered and angry, to be odd sorts who do not behave as other cats would. They almost live in a world of their own and may be subject to the same strange visual hallucinations as recorded in human patients. This may result in unexpected bouts of rage with delirious overtones and a desire to escape from their immediate surroundings. They are terribly fearful of being hurt or injured in any way.

## MY ELDERLY CAT GETS VERY ANXIOUS AT NIGHT

Few cats are genuinely worried by the dark. Many will sleep during the day and become active at night and their good eyesight enables them to get around without too much trouble. Unfortunately many older cats gradually lose their faculties through age, including eyesight which becomes less acute. Reasons include cataracts which can be a problem and retinal degeneration which is seen less frequently. There are a few homoeopathic remedies which do seem to help.

Phosphorus (The element) covers most of the problems mentioned. It is one of the remedies used to slow the development of cataracts, and is also indicated in retinal degeneration. In addition, phosphorus-type animals are extremely sensitive to external impressions and atmosphere, including a degree of trepidation on entering darkened areas.

Cannabis indica (East Indian Cannabis, Hashish) in its homoeopathic form (and definitely not illegal!) can be used for less manageable cats of an unpredictable nature. They are extremely vocal and seem unable to settle down, approaching at times a state of furious delirium. Feral cats often match this type for a while. Darkened space incites extreme fear.

Key features of cats who will benefit from stramonium (Thorn-apple) are a desire for company and a fear of the dark, much preferring the light. Yet mood swings are common, happy and contented one moment, angry and spitting the next, intent on escaping your clutches.

## MY CAT IS NEARING THE END OF ITS LIFE

Do cats sense that death is near? This is not an easy question to answer, but two homoeopathic remedies that have proved effective in the final closing stages of life are included here. It is likely that some cats do feel some sort of anxiety at such times, maybe picked up from their owners.

**Homoeopathic Remedies** (see pp. 8–10 for dosage and pp. 15–16 for administration)

Arsenicum album (White arsenic) can remove feelings of fear and anxiety and smooth the transition from this world into the next. It can be used in any situation regardless of the circumstances, but is likely to be more effective where a degree of anxiety or restlessness is noted.

Use ACONITE (Monkshood, Wolf's Bane) where there is extreme agitation and restlessness to the point that both owner and cat are becoming distressed. The anguish may be such that the cat cries out pitifully or moans. Attempts may be made to escape which only compound the problem. A few doses of aconite given at timely intervals can make a vast difference.

# *Fright: the Aftermath*

Reactions to frightening episodes and situations can persist for several days, weeks or even months. Some cats are never quite the same following a road accident or after a particularly traumatic tussle with an opponent. Mental scars remain and cannot always be spotted easily.

Physical problems can also develop, a phenomenon recognized in people which can also occur in cats. Hair loss, weight loss and self-mutilation are typical physical manifestations of psychological problems based on past trauma. These problems often respond to treatment using natural remedies.

**Homoeopathic Remedies** (see pp. 8–10 for dosage and pp. 15–16 for administration)

Used in high potency ACONITE (Monkshood, Wolf's Bane) can help with the more immediate consequences where the cat may seem fearful and agitated from an event that may have taken place some days earlier. The cat may even cower down attempting to hide, or tremble with fright.

Cats who respond to GELSEMIUM (Yellow jasmine) are rather timid by nature and apt to respond badly to fright or shocks, being cowards at heart. The possible consequences include incontinence, spraying or diarrhoea.

IGNATIA (St Ignatius Bean) Occasionally a severe fright can be the underlying cause of a more serious problem such as epilepsy or personality changes. If your cat is showing signs of this, then ignatia could well be the remedy to use. Typical patients are likely to be alert, nervous, hurried and easily excited, trembling with fright when cornered. Emotionally they are unstable and subject to changeable moods. Occasionally they may try to eat strange objects.

OPIUM (Latex from the opium poppy) A very clear indication for this remedy are ailments such as hair loss or behavioural changes and convulsions. Timorous cats who are frightened easily respond best, typically those which have been 'scared stiff'.

PHOS. AC. (Phosphoric acid) More suited to younger animals, this remedy can help cats who do not seem to be quite themselves following a mental or physical shock. They may seem listless, apathetic or indifferent, sometimes debilitated. Think of using phos. ac. in young rescue cats who have not been treated well and may be in poor condition, particularly if there is involuntary watery diarrhoea.

Where the cat seems anxious at night think of using COFFEA or BELLADONNA. Timid or very shy cats may also benefit from LYCOPODIUM, SILICEA or PULSATILLA.

**Bach Flower Remedies** (see p. 12 for dosage and pp. 15–16 for administration)

Use AGRIMONY (*Agrimonia eupatoria*) where the fears and worries are well hidden and outwardly, little appears wrong. However if worrying thoughts seem to persist, inducing an inner restlessness and turbulence, these may gradually impinge on everyday life and a change of temperament may become apparent. This may be seen as either aggression, impatience or restlessness.

STAR OF BETHLEHEM (*Ornithogalum umbellatum*) If your cat has undergone physical or mental trauma, irrespective of when the incident took place, use Star of Bethlehem for any consequences. It is one of the remedies included in RESCUE REMEDY and by many considered to be the most important. It can remove the effects of any past trauma and allow other remedies to work more effectively. Cats who benefit from Star of Bethlehem may move around in a sluggish subdued manner and almost appear depressed. This remedy revitalizes and renews life energy and removes obstructions to further healing providing both comfort and removing past sorrows.

# The Aloof, Unfriendly Cat

There are certain cats who consider themselves far superior to all around, whether feline or human. Consequently they do not always make the best of pets, as they like to keep themselves to themselves, and will accept only the best life has to offer. If you have the good fortune to own one of these animals, and would like it to be a little less difficult, it is worth trying some of the following remedies.

**Homoeopathic Remedies** (see pp. 8–10 for dosage and pp. 15–16 for administration)

LYCOPODIUM (Club moss) has many facets, including an association with feelings (or delusions) of superiority and resistance to any opposition. Intelligent cats, particularly exotics such as Siamese and Burmese, correspond to this type. They are very self-conscious and avoid crowds and unfamiliar faces. In contrast they often attach themselves to one particular person, revealing a certain degree of insecurity in their character make-up. Although seemingly quiet by nature, the arrogant side of their nature can be revealed in sudden outbursts of temper.

PLATINA (Platinum) Cats responding to PLATINA are more often female, exude self-importance and look with disdain upon all others. These stately-looking cats dislike interference and are very impatient. They can become possessive of one person and may pine in their absence.

VERATRUM ALBUM (White hellebore) Rather unpleasant cats liable to violent outbursts of rage almost to the point of mania may be helped with this remedy. Restlessness is a feature of theirs, revealing a relentless need to be occupied, which can lead to destructive behaviour. Delusions abound, including unfounded feelings of overall superiority to all others.

PALLADIUM (The metal) Another remedy for female cats with a definite arrogant side to their character. Despite their seemingly haughty character, however, they are actually very readily offended and their sense of pride is easily hurt.

SULPHUR (The element) The hungry, grubby-looking sulphur-type cat can sometimes surprisingly be somewhat arrogant. This goes paw in paw with a tendency to be rather lazy, stubborn and self-centred. Patience is also lacking in these short-tempered cats when things do not go the way they want.

**Bach Flower Remedies** (see p. 12 for dosage and pp. 15–16 for administration)

BEECH (*Fagus sylvatica*) Types who would respond to beech are intolerant of others, arrogant and standoffish. They lack understanding and have a very negative view of life which makes them tense, grumpy and short-tempered.

WATER VIOLET (*Hottonia palustris*) suits the well-bred Siamese, who have highly developed personalities and exude an air of superiority and calm. In this respect they appear almost un-approachable and do not seem to be the most ideal pets. They move silently in a dignified, reserved and ordered fashion, carefully selecting where they go and whom they approach.

Their straight unassailable character is not so upstanding as it may seem, and not surprisingly such cats suffer from a range of other psychological problems as their inner reserves are used up in maintaining their outward appearance. They resent interference and, when ill, would often rather be left alone than seek company. Typically they also find it difficult to accept other cats brought into a household as they maintain their poise and apparent indifference.

Water violet alters this situation and allows development of a more tolerant attitude and brings the cat down to earth, yet keeping an aura of inner dignity and an elegant appearance.

# Homesick Cats

We are not talking here of the human-type homesickness (which is more like feeling depressed and sad), but the homesickness cats feel when moving house and not adjusting well to their new environment.

Moving house is a traumatic experience for a cat, as it means changing familiar territory for the unknown. Many problems may arise, including SPRAYING (pp. 117–22) and SOILING (p. 123). You may also find your cat disappearing in search of its old home. Most of us have heard tales of cats travelling back over long distances to return to their old haunts.

It is worth taking simple precautions when you move house to minimize your cat's anxiety. The day you are to move, shut your cat into the bathroom of the old house, with food, water and a litter tray (placed away from the food). Since no furniture has to be moved from a bathroom, this will be the least disturbed place of the house, yet familiar.

When you are ready to move, make sure your cat travels with you (secured in a basket of course). And when you arrive, again shut it into a room that is unlikely to be disturbed by people moving about. Only when the house is quiet, let it out of the room but NOT out of the house, so that it can quietly explore its new surroundings. Keep it indoors for a few days before letting it out, and keep a close eye on it at first. You should then have very little trouble, provided you make plenty of fuss over your cat.

Apart from the possible problem of your cat bolting, there

are some cats who feel genuinely depressed over changes in their abode and feel unable to come to terms with them. It is worth trying these homoeopathic and Bach's Flower Remedies.

**Homoeopathic Remedies** (see pp. 8–10 for dosage and pp. 15–16 for administration)

CAPSICUM (Cayenne pepper) This is the most important homoeopathic remedy for homesickness. Cats most likely to respond are of a peevish nature and dislike company. They have probably always attached more importance to territory than to people anyway. In other words they feel miserable and depressed and not quite themselves. They tend to be lazy and stay inside most of the time brooding. Warmth and comfort is much appreciated; disruption and change of surroundings are not!

PHOS. ACID (Phosphoric acid) Younger cats who match this remedy, tend to be similar in character to those who respond to capsicum. Ill-humour abounds, together with a listless and indifferent nature. Excessive moulting, and a keen desire for milk may give a few clues to its use.

**Bach Flower Remedies** (see p. 12 for dosage and pp. 15–16 for administration)

HONEYSUCKLE (*Lonicera caprifolium*) Where honeysuckle may help, the cat's desire to return home is very strong, while its feelings of sadness are less prominent. The fundamental problem is a failure to accept the new changes and connect with the current situation. Such cats dwell on the past and literally spend a large part of their time trying to escape there both literally and mentally. Honeysuckle helps establish links with the present and strengthens acceptance of the changes.

# How to Cope with an Over-sexed Cat

Sexual problems amongst cats are rare and almost non-existent compared to the number of incidents of this type reported by dog owners. Most male cats are neutered before their hormones trigger any sexual exploits and consequently bizarre behaviour in neutered toms is practically unheard of. Occasionally un-neutered toms will try to mount other animals or items of furniture and, if castration is out of the question, then there are one or two remedies which may help. SPRAYING (pp. 117–22) even in neutered toms is of course a related problem and that is dealt with later.

Over-sexed females, on the other hand, are more of a problem. They call persistently and demand almost constant attention. Fortunately there are some homoeopathic remedies that can help in this area.

**Homoeopathic Remedies** (see pp. 8–10 for dosage and pp. 15–16 for administration)

LACHESIS (Bushmaster snake venom) is predominately a remedy for females and can be used to calm cats who are suspicious, jealous and aggressive by nature and who do not appreciate being fussed. It can be used to quell nymphomaniacal tendencies where such behaviour is easily excited.

GRATIOLA (Hedge hyssop) is a relatively little-known remedy that best suits cats with nymphomania. Normally they are of a serious, taciturn nature.

ORIGANUM (Sweet marjoram) Again a remedy for over-sexed female cats whose desires seem excessive and impulsive.

PLATINA (Platinum, the element) is a remedy for the more refined female, and helps those cats who consider themselves amongst the upper classes of the feline world and appear proud and haughty. Nymphomaniacal behaviour in exotic breeds such as Siamese may respond to this remedy.

PHOSPHORUS (The element) Of value to either male or female, where the general nature of the cat matches the 'phosphorus' personality – out-going, friendly, playful, attention-seeking and sensitive.

MUREX (The purple fish) Fairly well-orientated to females, murex will suit timorous, anxious cats, with an apprehensive nature coupled with an almost maniacal sexual desire that is triggered by the least stimulation.

PICRIC ACID (Trinitrophenol) Picric acid can be used to help the over-sexed male, especially those who get excited at the sight of any female. At other times they are lazy and disinclined to undertake much else.

# *Insomniac Cats*

Yes, some elderly cats do suffer from insomnia. As they lose their faculties older cats tend to feel more insecure. Their hearing is less acute and blindness can be a problem as well. They lose their agility as their muscles become stiff. Overall their general anxiety increases, and your elderly cat will come to rely more and more on you for protection and everyday care. As most of the day is spent sleeping in the knowledge that you are around, problems manifest themselves at night. When you go to bed, they begin to become active but realize they are alone. As a result they start seeking your attention by crying, wailing or door scratching. While some of the problems are psychologically based, it is important to recognize that some are also due to physical problems such as rheumatic pain.

Try where possible to encourage your cat to play and be active during the day, and give it lots of much needed attention. Hopefully, this will mean that your cat will sleep at night rather than being active. Don't always give in either. In certain cases, providing help in the middle of the night only reinforces their behaviour pattern. It may be better to ignore the problem in the hope that the cat will give in eventually when it realizes that its efforts are in vain.

**Herbal Remedies** (see p. 5 for dosage and p. 15–16 for administration)

These are invaluable for long-term use and provide a safe

alternative where homoeopathic remedies may be ineffective. Always ensure that your cat has no physical cause for it not sleeping well as the herbal remedies listed act more on a mental level.

VALERIAN (*Valeriana officinalis*) reduces anxiety and associated tension without causing drowsiness. It can help relieve hysteria and over-excitability and is one of the most useful herbal remedies in promoting sleep.

SKULLCAP (*Scutellaria laterifolia*) is often combined with valerian. It not only is a nerve tonic, but also an excellent sedative, calming anxiety and restlessness without drowsiness.

HOPS (*Humulus lupulus*) relax the nervous system generally and are recommended in the treatment of insomnia, helping reduce anxiety. This remedy can be combined with valerian and skullcap.

CHAMOMILE (German chamomile, *Matricaria chamomilla*) is very safe to use and renowned for its calming and relaxing properties. This makes it very suitable to use in older or frail cats. Its anti-inflammatory effect means that it will also ease abdominal pain.

**Homoeopathic Remedies** (see pp. 8–10 for dosage and pp. 15–16 for administration)

ARSENICUM ALBUM (Arsenious oxide, white arsenic) is probably the most important remedy in this context. Sleeplessness is due to feelings of anxiety which induce restlessness and an inability to remain in a single place for very long. The cat will settle in one place for a brief while and then get up and move around only to rest again for a short moment. There is a very strong desire for company and attention. Warmth is appreciated and will help relieve the symptoms.

In humans it is often said that dreams of, or fear of, death contribute to the anxiety, and the same may well be true of cats. Who knows?

ACONITE (Monkshood) should be used for general anxiety, especially where there is a degree of fear. It is a short-lasting remedy but can be given where there are no immediately obvious indications for another remedy.

NATRUM MURIATICUM (Common salt) has been used successfully where crying and wailing at night have been associated with grief. Although IGNATIA can also be used in this connection, nat. mur. works more effectively where symptoms have been evident at night. Thirst for large quantities of water and dislike of fuss and attention are other guides to its use.

CAUSTICUM (Potassium hydrate) is suited to the problems of old age, especially where there are general signs of senility and your cat's brain does not seem to be functioning as well as it used to be. At night the slightest noise may awaken your cat, and once awake it cannot get to sleep again as it is unable to get comfortable. This may be due to rheumatic pains in the limbs. Other notable features include loss of strength in the back legs and trembling.

BARIUM CARBONATE (Baryta carbonica) Old age problems can be alleviated with this remedy. Cats who respond to it often look older than they really are and characteristically seem to suffer from some form of senile dementia. This leads to confusion and poor memory and the consequent need for greater assistance and reassurance.

PULSATILLA (Wind flower) Here there is a great desire for company and restlessness. Cats who respond to pulsatilla are affectionate and gentle. Their timid nature means that they feel better for being comforted. Typically they tend to be awake in the early part of the evening.

RHUS TOX (Poison ivy) works where the insomnia is due to muscular or rheumatic pain. Relief will be obtained by making your cat move about as this eases the discomfort. Symptoms are worse in cold damp weather, and can be eased by warmth and a change of position.

KALI CARB. (Potassium carbonate) Where your cat keeps waking in the early hours (especially between two and four a.m.) and is unable to go back to sleep, try kali carb. Although this type of cat does not appreciate being fussed much, it does like to feel that someone is around.

COFFEA CRUDA is potentized coffee. We all know how coffee can keep us awake at night by stimulating the brain. In its homoeopathic form it can be used to quell overactivity. So use coffea in those older cats who are just too mentally alert at night, and for whom no other reason can be identified, or use it for those prone to become easily excited.

NUX VOMICA (Poison nut) is prescribed more on a constitutional (i.e. whole cat) basis. Nux vomica suits those cats of an irritable nature who are all keyed up and tense. They are usually of a thin lean build and very active. They are easily awoken by noises, especially in the early morning and once awake make sure that everyone else is as well. Their appetite is normally good but constipation can be a problem.

**Bach Flower Remedies** (see p. 12 for dosages and pp. 15–16 for administration)

MIMULUS (*Mimulus guttatus*) has proved to be one of the most useful in treating the insomniac cat. It is used to help treat specific fears that can be identified and often suits cats who are generally nervous by nature. In this case it is usually the fear of being left alone at night that causes the problems.

WHITE CHESTNUT (*Aesculus hippocastanum*) should be used where the cat will not relax due to some recent traumatic incident, such as after a severe fright or road accident. In this situation it is likely that persistent worrying thoughts keep racing through the cat's mind so that it cannot settle.

CHERRY PLUM (*Prunus cerasifera*) Sleeplessness associated with the general anxiety that can come with old age may respond to this remedy. As the older cat gradually loses its senses, particularly sight and hearing, then there is a fear of 'losing control', which often is accompanied by a lack of patience and irritability. Such cats will often parade around at night with persistent wailing and crying.

**Aromatherapy** (see p. 13 for application)

LAVENDER (*Lavandula officinalis*) can be used in one of two ways. Either by massage used in the late evening or by sprinkling a few drops of neat oil around the room where the cat is to sleep. This provides a general calming ambience.

CHAMOMILE (Roman chamomile, *Anthemis nobilis*) can be used as described for LAVENDER above. The keynote of chamomile is its soothing nature. It eases away aches and pains as well as settling an over-active mind and reducing anxiety and tension.

# *Feline Jealousy, Possessiveness and Hatred*

Possessiveness in a cat expresses itself as a selfish desire to have its owner totally to itself, and therefore an inability to share. The jealousy that arises when a new feline or a new person, or a baby is introduced into the household is centred around fear of being displaced, and can cause feelings of hatred. The cat may develop an intense dislike of a particular person or animal.

First and foremost, show your cat that it is just as much appreciated as it ever was. Make a fuss of it. Cats often feel their noses have been put out of joint and that they are neglected when, for example, a new baby arrives. Even if Mother does not have time for the cat, make sure that someone in the household does.

If you are introducing a new kitten, cuddle your old cat during the introductions. Instinctively, you may think you should be protecting the tiny kitten, but life will prove much easier afterwards, if you make more fuss of your old cat at this juncture. After cuddling it, allow the meeting to take place. Some bossy behaviour, including hissing and spitting, may occur initially – but it will occur sooner or later anyway. What is happening is merely your old cat establishing who's boss. Let this happen. The kitten will recognize its place in the 'pecking order' and all should be well.

If jealous behaviour continues, then resort to other

remedies. Jealousy at its worst can cause STRESS (pp. 124–32), SOILING (p. 123) or leaving home.

Fortunately a relatively small number of homoeopathic and Bach flower remedies have proved useful.

**Homoeopathy** (see pp. 8–10 for dosage and pp. 15–16 for administration)

APIS MELLIFICA (The honey bee) The cat who responds to apis has a somewhat unpredictable nature and is easily upset by emotional changes or stress. They are usually restless, fidgety, suspicious and sometimes clumsy. There is a definite dislike of being touched to the point of being aggressive, yet a desire for company – but not affection. Despite these characteristics the apis cat is surprisingly jealous, often becoming attached to one person in particular.

LACHESIS (Bushmaster snake venom) Use lachesis where feelings of jealousy are more obvious and there is also a sense of hatred. By nature cats who respond tend to be extremely anxious and suspicious, and, more often than not, there is a great sensitivity to both noise and of being handled. There is a close link to the way the snake behaves in real life and the way the 'lachesis' cat acts, often lashing out unpredictably when least expected. Just as the bushmaster's tongue flickers in and out mimicking speech, cats which respond well usually have a lot to say for themselves.

HYOSCYAMUS (Henbane, *Hyoscyamus niger*) is associated with a degree of suspicion, mania and aggression, with a number of distinguishing features which sets it apart from other remedies. There is a keen desire for warmth and a dislike of being alone, yet when jealous feelings are aroused the character can change rapidly. The inherent quarrelsome nature takes over as the cat's pupils dilate and a state of rage ensues. Watch out for the claws and teeth as the pent-up anger is vented on the unsuspecting culprit.

PULSATILLA (Wind flower) The affectionate, yielding, timid nature of the 'pulsatilla' cat is a complete contrast to that of hyoscyamus. Pulsatilla individuals are often female and the most gentle of cats with a great desire for company, human or otherwise. Solitude is avoided at all costs and affection is gratefully absorbed. Hardly ever violent they are prone none the less to mood swings which bear comparison to the way the plant behaves in the wind – first blowing this way then the other. They are certainly capable of feelings of jealousy and envy when they are no longer the sole recipient of affection.

ARSENICUM ALBUM (Arsenious oxide, white arsenic) is valuable where possessiveness seems to be the main problem. The cat who will respond well to this has some specific features which help as a guide to its use. They are usually apprehensive and restless in character with a certain unease about them. Above all they spend a disproportionate amount of time on grooming and always looking neat and clean. 'Arsenicum' cats lead well-ordered lives and are extremely sensitive to disruption and disorder. Their need for company is also prominent and where there is competition for attention problems can arise.

NATRUM MURIATICUM (Sodium chloride, common salt) It is surprising to learn that a common everyday substance such as salt can be used to treat feline psychological problems but NAT. MUR. is associated with hatred and in the right situations can prove invaluable. Cats who respond well keep themselves to themselves and only ever seek affection when they want it. They are definitely not lap cats and avidly dislike fuss and attention. Despite eating exceptionally well they are usually of lean build and of energetic personality, occasionally given to bouts of gloom. Once crossed, they are apt to harbour resentment and deep dislike of another, be it cat or human.

**Bach Flower Remedies** (see pp. 12 for dosage and pp. 15–16 for administration)

HOLLY (*Ilex aquifolium*) With its thick, glossy, leathery leaves and stout prickles, holly matches well the spiky, robust nature of those cats who benefit from its use. It is the single most important remedy, covering possessiveness, jealousy and hatred. Where these attitudes predominate, then holly will help with the inevitable consequences as well – aggression, suspicion and lack of tolerance.

BEECH (*Fagus sylvatica*) is sometimes a useful addition to HOLLY. This remedy suits cats that demand order in their lives and respond badly to changes such as the introduction of a new animal into the household. Their intolerance is often manifested by becoming anti-social, avoiding fuss and attention, sometimes promoting their aggressive nature.

CHICORY (*Cichorium intybus*) The jealousy associated with this remedy centres around the egotistic, possessive attitude of the 'chicory' type of cat. These pretentious felines demand full and unerring attention which is not, at any cost, to be shared with any other cats. In fact they are fundamentally selfish at heart and find it hard to share their lives with any other animal. They may even get very angry if they cannot get their own way.

**Aromatherapy** (see pp. 13–14 for application)

JASMINE (*Jasminum officinale*) is one of the more expensive oils and can induce a feeling of euphoria, and allow emotional expression. It is useful where jealousy is a problem.

YLANG YLANG (*Cananga odorata*) is another oil indicated in relieving the feelings of jealousy, at the same time inspiring confidence.

GRAPEFRUIT (*Citrus paradisi*) is linked with possessiveness, jealousy, bitterness and frustration. It has an uplifting nature and can help relieve all of these unwanted feelings.

---

*Sherry, a six-year-old tortoiseshell, had always been an odd sort of cat. Living on a farm she had absolute freedom and could wander and do as she pleased. She was certainly not keen on fuss, and naturally suspicious, lurking in corners, carefully observing the approach of any strangers who entered her domain. Needless to say, trips to the vet were a nightmare, as Sherry's short temper let loose its full fury on the least provocation. Major problems developed when a new baby arrived in the household, as Sherry sensed a change in the daily routine and perceived the child as a threat to her position in the household. Her character changed for the worse, becoming even more short-tempered than usual, with an unerring desire to 'see off' her rival, to which she added a spate of vocal abuse. Her selfish, anxious, suspicious traits, her dislike of being handled and talkative nature suggested LACHESIS as a suitable remedy. Sherry received lachesis 30 twice daily for ten days followed by the 200 potency three times weekly for four weeks. This resolved her jealousy problem completely.*

# Manic Cats

This does *not* refer to the zany spells that many Siamese cats have, where, at a certain time of day, they rush madly around, bouncing off walls and furniture, genuinely having fun and showing off with their acrobatics. Here we are talking of really strange behaviour characterized by great excitement, accompanied by bouts of violence. Fortunately maniacal cats are few and far between, but definitely exist, as their owners well know. Their behaviour is exceptional, often bizarre and totally irrational. With unpredictable mood swings and an aggressive and destructive attitude, they are understandably not always that easy to live with. Homoeopathic remedies can, however, help significantly in dealing with some of the more worrying aspects of this behavioural problem.

**Homoeopathic Remedies** (see pp. 8–10 for dosage and pp. 15–16 for administration)

BELLADONNA (Deadly nightshade) will benefit cats who are easily startled by the least noise or unexpected movement. They are likely to become excited and may rush around in a heated, uncontrollable frenzy, attempting to bite or scratch. If trapped or cornered they may scrabble frantically in a destructive manner to escape. As quickly as the manic episodes arise, they may subside and the cat will lapse into a period of quiet.

'Belladonna' type cats seem to always live in a state of

turmoil. Their anger is easily aroused, and they seem hot, hurried and excited with a propensity to bite, injure, spit or just escape and run off.

HYOSCYAMUS (Henbane) The heat and congestion associated with BELLADONNA is not so prominent where this remedy is concerned, where the key pointers to its use include jealousy and suspicion. Strange fears probably abound making the cat behave in a curious fashion, sometimes as if pursued by something unknown, chasing around a room endlessly for no clear reason. Anger when aroused can lead to very violent behaviour with a desire to fight and actually kill an opponent. Sudden outbursts of rage can result in seemingly endless vocalization with restless searching for the opportunity to escape and inflict damage on whoever is closest.

STRAMONIUM (Thorn-apple) is associated with frenzy and violent behaviour, in fact the most violent of all three remedies given in this section. The cat may look terrified and become particularly wildly excited if plunged into darkness or if left alone. Underlying this behaviour are probably some sort of irrational fears and imaginary images as experienced in humans that respond to this remedy. This state of delirium causes the cat to act completely out of character in a crazy manner where sense of reason is lost. Warmth, company and light can help calm the situation.

---

*The Jekyll and Hyde of the cat world probably lives in a small peaceful resort on the coast. When Mouse arrived, recently moved from a city, she seemed to settle in well and caused no particular problems either for her owners or the neighbours and their resident felines. She shared the house with one other younger cat called William. There was no doubt who was boss – Mouse.*

*After a few months, just after her twelfth birthday, Mouse began to act strangely, initially setting upon William and either clawing or biting him for what seemed no obvious reason. They had, after all, lived together quite happily for many years. Her behaviour became more bizarre as time passed, with sudden frenzied dashes across the garden and mock fights with the plant life there. Some of her attacks were incredibly intense, inflicting severe damage on the plants. The situation became more worrying as these amazingly violent outbursts extended to William and then the neighbours' cats.*

*Yet in between these odd bouts she behaved normally and was very affectionate and loving, even to William. Gradually the good periods became fewer and fewer and her antics more and more bizarre. A pattern developed as each attack was preceded by loud deafening crying and pacing up and down, culminating in a surprising outburst of activity, always violent and unpredictable. A cry for help was sent out when Mouse mounted a frenzied raid on a neighbour's garden gnome, resulting in its complete annihilation.*

*HYOSCYAMUS matched the symptoms well, and this was prescribed in increasing potencies from 30c to 1M over a period of several weeks. The response was gratifying, and little by little Mouse returned to normality as the crazy episodes grew less and less extreme and more infrequent. Eventually Mouse began to behave more like her old self, much to the relief of all around, although she still needed the occasional dose of hyoscyamus as she tended to relapse from time to time. At least all the gnomes in the vicinity felt safe in the knowledge that the 'mad cat' was no longer on the lookout for trouble.*

# Aggressive Mothers

Some queens will occasionally reject their kittens for no apparent reason. A closer look, however, reveals two causes. The first is lack of energy and general interest, caused by the stress and trauma of kittening. The second is a genuine change in the cat's mental state, resulting in a failure of the mother-kitten bond to develop. Some cases may be due to hormonal changes, particularly the fall in progesterone that follows kittening. These changes may induce aggressive feelings (which to some extent are normal in terms of protecting the newborn) or intolerance of other cats, which may include offspring. Different causes need different solutions and the following have proved of great help.

**Homoeopathic Remedies** (see pp. 8–10 for dosages and pp. 15–16 for administration)

KALI CARB. (Potassium carbonate) is a general remedy, which acts more on the physical aspect, and is more suited to cats of an irritable nature and those who appear sensitive to pain. It can help post-kittening with exhaustion and general weakness.

SEPIA (Ink of the cuttlefish) The type of cat suited to treatment with sepia is apathetic and indifferent, showing a desire to get away from people, even those who are familiar and loved. This trait can unfortunately be carried over to newborn offspring who may be rejected from the very moment they arrive. Not only that, but they are usually sad irritable characters as well and not the most ideal mothers. Sepia may help and can often induce maternal feelings in those queens who have none.

HELLEBORUS (The Snow Rose or Christmas Rose) suits those queens who seem sad, miserable and sluggish and show a degree of apathy that extends to the care of their kittens. Everything is an effort and anger is easily aroused.

PLATINA (The metal) is another remedy pre-eminently suited to females. The keynote to its use is a degree of arrogance. Platina cats reckon on being a cut above other cats and like to show it. They appear proud, haughty and contemptuous. This remedy often suits Siamese cats. The bad side to their nature is expressed as a destructive influence, that may show as temptation to injure the kittens.

**Bach Flower Remedies** (see p. 12 for dosage and pp. 15–16 for administration)

RESCUE REMEDY is to be used after any kittening, not only for the mother, but for the kittens as well. Not only does it assist healing but it can calm and pacify, in addition to helping restore inherent energy.

OLIVE (*Olea europoea*) is of most value where the kittening has been long and protracted; energy reserves are low, both on the physical and mental side. Exhaustion of mind, body and spirit has resulted, and interest in the new arrivals is not aroused. Olive helps restore the balance of all aspects once more.

WILD ROSE (*Rosa canina*) Cats responding to this show a degree of apathy and general lack of interest in life *per se.*

After the birth of the kittens they appear to have given up even before they have started. They feel no joy or pleasure in the birth and show no concern about the kittens at all. Kittens or no kittens, life continues in its same old boring routine. Try wild rose and see what happens.

ELM (*Ulmus procera*) In contrast to the apathetic WILD ROSE type of cat, elm is undoubtedly useful to those queens overwhelmed by the experience of kittening. Considered normal in every other aspect of life, young queens can find instant motherhood just a little too much to live with. This temporary feeling of inadequacy responds well to elm. Feelings of exhaustion and despondency are transformed into confidence and a sense of responsibility, and all is well.

# *Pining*

We all develop strong emotional bonds, sometimes unconsciously, between ourselves and our companion animals. Often without realizing it, we become very attached to our pets. This union is two-way and cats may well become just as attached to us. Not only that, but they often become emotionally entangled with other animals and not always those sharing the same house.

The loss of a companion is always a difficult time emotionally and is just as much so for domestic cats. They will grieve or pine just as we might do, and it is made worse because they cannot understand what is happening. As much as we might try, we cannot tell them what is going on. Prolonged worry can result in strange changes in behaviour that can be very distressing to see. There can be physical effects as well. This can amount to anything from the development of skin problems, poor appetite to weight loss or kidney failure. It can take anything up to six months for them to come out of the grieving period. Gentle stroking, talking to your cat and keeping it company will help a great deal. Natural remedies have a great part to play here in a condition that is very difficult to treat conventionally.

*Furface, a large neutered black and white tom, arrived through the cat-flap and took up residence on an unused chair tucked under the kitchen table, where he was not discovered for several days. Although Pussycat, the elder of the resident cats, disliked him on sight and continued to tell him so, Furface and Pussycat's son, T. Kitten Esquire, developed a workable relationship. Eventually Pussycat died, and a year later so did her son, T. Kitten. On his death, Furface was bereft. He cowered under a chair for days, trembling and refusing to eat. His fur became brittle and developed bald patches. Only lots of cuddles and affection brought him back to normal. Eventually a tortoiseshell kitten was found to keep him company and they became terrific pals.*

**Homoeopathic Remedies** (see pp. 8–10 for dosage and pp. 15–16 for administration)

IGNATIA (St Ignatius Bean) is the most important homoeopathic remedy for treating pining and grief. It acts at a deep level and can sometimes bring hidden emotions to the surface. Use it in any situation where there has been a loss of a companion, even if outward signs are absent. Some cats show sudden emotional and behavioural changes at these times and it is easy to spot the change and link it with recent happenings. Others will conceal their emotions well and suffer grief in silence. Give IGNATIA in both situations.

NATRUM MURIATICUM (Common salt) Both outward and inward grieving can respond to NAT. MUR. and this remedy can be given after IGNATIA if need be. It works better in cats who are somewhat irritable and seem depressed. Typically they want to be left alone to suffer in silence. They hate fuss and will only tolerate interference on their own terms. Other indications are unusual changes in general health. Look for an increase in thirst or appetite and possibly a loss of weight. Kidney problems which arise after the loss of a companion may respond.

PULSATILLA (Wind flower) Whereas cats likely to respond to NAT. MUR. are not keen on attention, pulsatilla-type cats crave fuss. They are shy and sensitive by nature and are apt to suffer grief in silence, carefully hiding away their emotions from the outside world. Normally they drink very little and quite like being in the fresh air.

STAPHYSAGRIA (Stavesacre) has a wide number of applications including the treatment of grief. It is particularly useful where physical problems are apparent, more than outward emotional changes. Skin problems are the most common and include the sudden appearance of itchy scabs over the back, or hair loss extending down the back legs.

AURUM (Metallic gold) Where deep depression is suspected, try aurum. This type of cat was once playful and happy and now lies around all day looking sad and dejected. They tend to be sensitive to noise, confusion and excitement.

CAUSTICUM (Potassium hydrate) Cats suited to causticum treatment are easily upset emotionally and occasionally prone to hysterical outbursts. Like AURUM-cats they are sensitive to noise and anything unusual or different. This situation may develop gradually over a long period as a result of long-lasting grief or worry. The consequences of prolonged emotional strain can affect general health. Use causticum where the ageing process seems to have suddenly taken hold following the loss of a companion.

**Bach Flower Remedies** (see p. 12 for dosage and pp. 15–16 for administration)

STAR OF BETHLEHEM (*Ornithogalum umbellatum*) is to be used in the initial stages where the impact of the loss is most. The cat will seem unhappy, disorientated and may appear lost. It is not unusual at this point for a cat to search tirelessly for a lost friend. Star of Bethlehem will reduce feelings of sadness, clear the mind and give inner strength to cope with the situation.

RED CHESTNUT (*Aesculus carnea*) helps to deal with the worry aspect of the loss. Its keynote is over-concern for others. This situation arises from an over-attachment to another animal or a person, usually the owner. When they disappear for whatever reason the cat immediately worries even if there is actually nothing really amiss. In the context of grief its use allows them to accept the loss and stop brooding and at the same time induces feelings of well-being and security.

OLIVE (*Olea europoea*) Mind, spirit and body can be drained by prolonged worry or strain following the loss of a close companion. Cats will pine to the point of making themselves ill, neither eating or drinking for days on end, gradually wasting away. Exotic cats, particularly Siamese and Burmese will do this to the point of near-death sometimes. In this situation, add olive to any other remedy to improve strength, vitality and inner energy.

**Aromatherapy** (see pp. 13–14 for application)

HYSSOP (*Hyssopus officinalis*) has the ability to help stabilize any situation where imbalance is evident. This includes grief situations in particular. Use only very small amounts – four times the usual dilution – for massage. Do not use it on epileptic or pregnant cats.

ROSE (*Rosa centifolia*) is cleansing both physically and mentally, and can be used as an alternative to hyssop. It will induce a feeling of well-being, and help an animal come to terms with the current situation.

CHAMOMILE (*Anthemis nobilis*) will help your cat when it is very distressed and alarmed by the sudden change in its seemingly ordered life. It is very soothing and calming and can be invaluable where there is great mental restlessness and physical over-activity.

---

*Ying and Yang were two country-dwelling Burmese cats whose owners moved into town. Although they settled into their new home well, Yang (who had little road sense) was involved in an accident with a car and unfortunately died.*

*The two cats were brothers, and were very close. Ying missed his brother immediately. He searched the house and garden endlessly, looking for his companion, but of course had no idea of what had happened. At times he would sit at the bottom of the garden just calling out pitifully.*

*Seeing Ying visibly distressed, his owners gave him* STAR OF BETHLEHEM *which seemed to help. After a few days he stopped looking and seemed to accept that his brother was no longer around.*

*Ying normally ate and drank well, but about a week later he stopped eating altogether and drank virtually nothing. Despite this he appeared quite bright in himself. Fearing that he was ill, his owner took him to the vet who was unable to find the exact cause of the problem. Antibiotics and vitamins were prescribed but with no result. Ying began to lose weight and became lethargic. Blood tests failed to identify a cause and further treatment failed to elicit any change.* (cont.)

(cont.)

*The problem was psychological and related to the loss of his brother. IGNATIA was prescribed in the 30 potency twice daily for five days based on the assumption that Ying was suffering from inwardly directed grief. After the first dose there was a visible change for the better. He started to eat and began to take an interest in life once more. After five days' treatment he was almost his former self. Further homoeopathic treatment was given to resolve the problem once and for all. Ying received five doses of ignatia 200, spaced out over a period of two weeks after which all was well.*

# Resentment and Indignation

Do cats suffer feelings of resentment and indignation? The answer is a very definite yes, although they can be very good at hiding their emotions, but nonetheless can feel bitter, aggrieved, suffer anger and scorn and feel unjustly done by. When do these situations arise?

Indignation and resentment occur most commonly after neutering and other surgery, following accidents, changes in circumstances (such as moving house or introducing new animals into a household), after a change in daily routine, following a stay in the cattery, a temporary separation from their owner, or territorial disputes.

Many people are all too aware of the consequences of an unfamiliar cat entering the house, as their once clean cat starts suddenly SPRAYING (see pp. 117–22).

Spraying aside, the cat's response, whatever the initial cause, can take one of two other courses. There can be a remarkable yet distressing change in temperament, with the emergence of an intolerant, angry and irritable animal from a once placid individual. This change is easily spotted. Unfortunately some cats are unable to express their feelings outwardly and consequently inwardly brood over wrongs or insults. Rage or fury burn within, with no vent for such feelings. It is this group who develop physical illness, the most common of which is the development of skin problems. Fortunately where the problem can be identified, it can be treated.

**Homoeopathy** (see pp. 8–10 for dosage and pp. 15–16 for administration)

STAPHYSAGRIA (Stavesacre) is the best homoeopathic remedy to help sort out feelings of resentment, indignation or bitterness, and covers both mental and physical aspects.

Where the mental symptoms are uppermost, it will help feelings of anger and its ensuing outbursts of violence. These cats are often very sensitive and easily upset. A trip in a basket to the vet's with prodding and poking can just tip them over the edge. They remain in a bad frame of mind for the rest of the day. Definitely not to be disturbed! The same applies post surgery. Many owners will have encountered the return of a somewhat angry feline having had 'the operation' and almost certainly experiencing some degree of pain. Again avoid handling! Luckily staphysagria can help in calming both the anger and the pain, particularly when combined with a little peace and quiet in a warm place.

It can also help those cats who are unable to express their feelings outwardly: they brood silently over an insult or wounded pride, and as a result of this may develop skin lesions. Normally such problems arise shortly after neutering, with the development of scabs and sore areas. These areas irritate, causing the cat to itch and scratch. The condition is diagnosed conventionally as miliary eczema and often treated with hormone tablets. A great many cases, however, will respond to staphysagria.

Don't forget that this remedy can also be useful in other situations where there is a degree of indignation or resentment: where your cat doesn't appear to be totally back to normal even if the suspect incident was several months in the past, following any sort of surgery, an accident, a stay in a boarding cattery, or a new addition to the household.

COLOCYNTHIS (Bitter cucumber) The indications for colocynthis are very similar to STAPHYSAGRIA, but it is used much less frequently. It suits irritable cats who flare up easily and want to be left alone. They are readily upset and subject to emotional disturbances and suffer the consequences thereof. Indignation causes anger. Where pain is involved colocynthis can ease the situation, especially where the discomfort is such that it causes the cat to curl up in a tight ball. Where STAPHYSAGRIA can help with associated skin problems, colocynthis-cats may produce a jelly-like covering to their stools as a result of unexpressed feelings.

NUX VOMICA (Poison nut) can sometimes also be used where the personality matches the individual. Cats who respond are anxious, irritable and tense by nature and easily upset by noises, bright lights and being disturbed or picked up. They are usually of lean build despite a good appetite and have a great desire to be warm. After an insult they are apt to feel sorry for themselves, but consolation is not appreciated.

**Bach Flower Remedies** (see p. 12 for dosage and pp. 15–16 for administration)

WILLOW (*Salix vitellina*) suits resentment and embitterment. From time to time many cats will feel angered and resentful over events occurring in everyday life. Such feelings can be quite transient but there can be a destructive effect where such feelings linger. The result is a sullen, moody moggie who is somewhat touchy. Bitterness is felt deep inside, feeling sorry for itself, equivalent to what we would understand as the 'poor old me' attitude. We know that where the feelings cannot be expressed, then external symptoms of illness can appear.

Willow is another way of treating the problem, breaking the negativity that surrounds the feelings of resentment and indignation. This remedy particularly suits those cats whose thoughts are turned inwards and whose anger smoulders inside with no vent. Willow allows recognition and acceptance of past events and harmonization of the cat's emotions. The result is a happier cat.

HOLLY (*Ilex aquifolium*) can be used successfully in this field and is, in a way, opposite to willow. Just as the willow cat is more passive, turning emotions inwards, then holly gives air to feelings immediately and in a very active fashion. Understandably avoid the teeth and claws.

# Cowardly Cats

A number of cats are shy by nature and not terribly brave. They hide away unseen or run for cover when a stranger enters the house. They are not very good at sticking up for themselves and may get picked upon by other cats, sometimes even those living in the same household. Away from home they cower and tremble when looked at and would really rather hide away out of sight. Some of these are fundamentally cowards at heart.

Rescued cats often act this way when first caught or rehomed. This is not surprising considering their change in circumstances and the fact that many of them may well have been mistreated. Of course they are not sure of what is going to happen and act accordingly either in an aggressive or submissive way. It is not unknown for a cat to hide away in a corner or in some little nook for days on end. This is not cowardice of course, but more related to the uncertainty or anxiety with regard to the future. If the new cat you have acquired seems too shy to come to you, maybe you have been using the wrong approach (see p. 56)

Some of the remedies listed elsewhere, particularly in the fears and phobias section, can be a great help. Check the homoeopathic remedies ARGENTUM NITRICUM (p. 51) and GELSEMIUM (pp. 51–2) and look up MIMULUS (pp. 55–6) and ASPEN (p. 54) which are both Bach flower remedies.

> *Freddie and Lisa were found as tiny kittens inside a plastic bag with their two dead siblings, on a skip, and taken to an animal rescue centre. Despite much loving attention and affection from their subsequent caring owners, both cats remained very shy and apprehensive. Lisa eventually took to her heels and disappeared altogether. Freddie, now six years old and with a new companion called George, still runs to hide under the sofa when anyone comes to the house. Freddie would benefit from some of these remedies.*

**Homoeopathic Remedies** (see pp. 8–10 for dosages and pp. 15–16 for administration)

SILICEA (Flint) The cat who will respond to silicea is essentially shy and apprehensive, lacking in confidence and initiative. They lack drive and although often intelligent tend to be lazy. Sometimes their inadequacies are coupled with a touchy, irritable nature. They dislike being looked at and on occasion may try to bite when touched. More often the opposite is the case, with the timid little cat curling up and remaining completely passive when examined. Underlying this nature is a fear of failure and sensitivity to various stimuli, especially sudden noises. Appetite is often poor, thirst is often above average and there is a tendency to catch recurrent infections as their resistance is low.

PULSATILLA (Wind flower) Gentle, yielding, affectionate female cats suit pulsatilla. They are fond of company and affection and dislike being alone. Yet although they may appear anxious, they are bashful or timid rather than nervous. They are easily offended and would rather run than confront an opponent.

SULPHUR (The element) On occasion the untidy, none-too-clean-looking, lazy sulphur-cat can be a little bashful and shy. This type is usually more selfish and self-centred and apt to become heated and angry. Its coat is usually poor and there may be concurrent problems with the skin such as dermatitis.

BARYTA CARB. (Barium carbonate) is more suited to younger cats and kittens, slower and more backward animals, who appear slightly retarded and not so intelligent. Part of this is due to a shy, timid nature which leads to inactivity and concurrent lack of interest and part due to vague fears that something might happen.

AMBRA GRISEA (Ambergris formed in the intestinal tract of the whale) Great timidity and intense shyness are associated with this unusual remedy: the cat may hide away a great deal and pointedly avoid company, particularly of strangers. The cat is easily upset and very sensitive, resulting in violent aggressive outbursts. In the past ambra grisea has been able to help cats who are reluctant to use litter trays in their owner's presence, almost as if they were embarrassed to be seen using it in public!

ANACARDIUM (Marking nut) is associated with poor memory and lack of confidence. This leads to an angry ill-humoured cat, who is inclined to hurry from place to place, not really quite sure where to go or what to do.

**Bach Flower Remedies** (see p. 12 for dosages and pp. 15–16 for administration)

LARCH (*Larix decidua*) Very timid cats with an inferiority complex often benefit from larch, as will those who cling to their owners or hide away, avoiding all contact. It is also worth considering for cats who are repeatedly attacked and who are not able to defend themselves well. Their defeatist attitude means that they expect to lose and therefore do not put up any resistance. This leads to a hesitant, passive nature and lack of drive.

CERATO (*Ceratostigma willmottiana*) Younger kittens often need this remedy, especially when growing up amongst other cats. They are unable to form their own ideas and are easily led by other more forward animals. Outwardly they appear stupid or simple and are sometimes the smallest in the litter. Cerato boosts confidence and can result in a cat being more determined to survive.

WILD OAT (*Bromus ramosus*) has helped cats who have been introduced into multi-cat households where the hierarchy is already set up and the newcomer does not know where to fit in exactly. In human terms it helps one to determine one's way in life, relieving a degree of uncertainty about the future. Cats can have exactly the same feelings when confronted by a well-ordered feline household.

CENTAURY (*Centaurium erythraea*) type cats are weak-willed because their personality is not well developed. They are often set upon by cats and rank low in the feline pecking order. Some owners describe them as cowards which to some extent is actually true, as they are really not capable of standing up for themselves and would rather run and hide, than fight and defend their territory. As pets they are good-natured and easy to deal with. They hardly ever cause problems, except all the occasions spent visiting the vet to get patched up again after the latest fight.

**Aromatherapy** (see p. 13 for application)

JASMINE (*Jasminum officinale*) Use in massage or vaporized. It produces feelings of optimism, happiness and helps instil confidence.

YLANG YLANG (*Cananga odorata*) is a warming, exotic oil that produces confidence and relieves stress.

# *Slow-on-the-uptake Cats*

In nearly every litter of kittens there is one which is weaker than all the others. Many survive, but as it grows it is obvious that it is somewhat backward in terms of both physical and mental development. The following selection of remedies can help.

**Homoeopathic Remedies** (see pp. 8–10 for dosages and pp. 15–16 for administration)

BARYTA CARB. (Barium carbonate) is the most useful of all the remedies. It can help kittens who appear slightly emaciated, with bulging stomachs and weak digestive systems. Occasionally there is a history of throat problems with enlarged glands. Memory and co-ordination are poor and they are apt to be timid, shy creatures. They are late in learning and initially take little interest in their environment.

AETHUSA CYNAPIUM (Fool's parsley) can be helpful to young cats who cannot digest milk, resulting either in diarrhoea or vomiting. Where vomiting occurs it is usually of white frothy material or curds. The kitten is restless and cries often, seems unable to rest and may actually become quite irritable at times. Learning is slow and confusion is obvious.

PLUMBUM (Lead) can help where there is leg weakness, almost paralysis of the hind limbs. Perception is slow and the kitten may appear depressed, sad and dejected. Memory is weak and may lead to confusion. It is well matched to weak, emaciated, anaemic kittens but obviously veterinary care will be required here to help as well.

PHOS. ACID (Phosphoric acid) Both physical and mental debility are evident where phosphoric acid can be of use. It can help debilitated backward kittens who are slow, apathetic and indifferent. Appetite is poor and diarrhoea is nearly always a feature. The stomach may be distended with gas which may be passed along with involuntary watery stools.

SILICEA (Pure flint) type kittens appear sickly and small. Sometimes their head may appear a little too large for their body. Learning is slow and they never seem to do well. They lack 'go' or initiative and are always the last to venture any distance from their mother. The general state of weakness means that wounds are apt to become infected easily and that their general resistance is low. Warmth and security are always sought at any cost.

**Bach Flower Remedies** (see p. 12 for dosages and pp. 15–16 for administration)

CHESTNUT BUD (*Aesculus hippocastanum*) relates to learning capacity and the inability to adapt to life through experience. There is a learning block and the same problem occurs again and again as the kitten fails to gain from its encounters in life. Development is retarded and the cat may appear awkward and ill-adapted for its age.

This remedy transforms this state, increasing mental activity and ability to comprehend and learn. Attention is finally focused on the present.

CLEMATIS (*Clematis vitalba*) Slightly older kittens may benefit from clematis, those who seem dreamy and not altogether in the real world. They sometimes seem confused, lack vitality and may appear apathetic. Clumsy movements are occasionally noted as the senses fail to become tuned into the current situation. A point to note is that the natural instinct for self-preservation is poor.

**Aromatherapy** (see pp. 13–14 for application)

ROSEMARY (*Rosmarinus officinalis*) Its general stimulant properties are useful in providing help to seemingly slow kittens. Rosemary provides both mental and physical support, improving not only circulation and digestion but also aiding concentration, and counteracting indecision, mental fatigue and disorientation. Never apply directly even in dilute form, rather sprinkle a little around the bedding area.

# Spraying

Cats who spray indoors can be a nightmare. Not only do they choose the choicest spots, but often select the most inaccessible areas or most expensive items to mark. Spraying is a very deliberate act and not to be confused with other forms of indoor urination caused by other psychological problems, or with involuntary urination due to old age.

Cats naturally start spraying when they reach adolescence at around eight or nine months of age. Both males and females spray, but tomcats have the most pungent urine and are the more prolific sprayers. The onset of this behaviour is hormonally related and spraying is normally used to mark outside territory. Although neutering reduces the frequency of spraying and the pungency of the urine (and aggressiveness in males), both neutered males and females continue to spray as part of their normal behavioural routine.

The inclination to spray varies not only between individual cats but also with breed. Cats of Oriental breeding are likely to spray more, as are more nervous animals. Each individual will have a certain threshold, which if exceeded will trigger off a bout of spraying. Different cats have different triggers. For some it is the introduction of a new cat into the house, for others a change in daily routine or just an increase in their general level of anxiety (after an encounter with an aggressive adversary for example). The act of spraying surrounds the cat in its own aroma, increasing its sense of security and reducing anxiety. It is only when spraying starts indoors that we begin to take notice!

Most cats perceive 'home' as a safe haven: a place to relax away from life outside the cat-flap, and usually do not spray indoors for obvious reasons – there is no need. If their sanctum is violated by an intruder, deliberately introduced or entering illicitly, then the cat's natural response will be to spray, in an effort to provide self-reassurance, increase confidence and to ensure that the ground is tagged as being the rightful owner's and not belonging to anybody else.

Your obvious solution here will be to try to stop the intruding cat, sometimes the only solution being to purchase an electronic cat-flap which will admit only your own cats, wearing electronic tags. Whilst this example has an easily identifiable straightforward trigger factor, we know that there are also a variety of other incentives that may prompt the potential sprayer to embark upon a course that will make life difficult for all concerned. Rather than list all of these here, we have dealt with them under the appropriate remedies.

**Homoeopathic Remedies** (see pp. 8–10 for dosage and pp. 15–16 for administration)

STAPHYSAGRIA (Stavesacre) is the best remedy to use in this context and may still be effective even if the incident in question took place some months before. It is suitable for a cat who displays resentment and indignation, working on inner feelings and suppressed anger that arise after the intrusion of an unfamiliar cat on to 'private property', sometimes only the garden; a more serious violation acting as the trigger, is another cat entering through the cat-flap. The result is a fervent bout of spraying as a way of expressing the incumbent's feelings.

The same feeling of resentment can arise in other situations. Introducing a new cat into the household or punishment for misdemeanours can start some cats spraying. Others have started after encountering a burglar face to face. Staphysagria may well solve the problem. Occasionally cats have been known to start spraying shortly after neutering (both males and females); once again, try staphysagria.

USTILAGO (The Corn-smut) is a much less well known remedy but has been successful in controlling spraying in males. It probably works by reducing some of the inherent male desires which include a propensity to spray. If STAPHYSAGRIA does not appear to work it is certainly worth trying.

FOLLICULINUM (a potentized ovarian hormone), OESTROGEN (potentized oestrogen) and TESTOSTERONE (potentized testosterone). All these remedies are produced from potentized hormones and on occasion have been used to treat unmanageable neutered animals. They may well work by modifying behaviour in some way. It is best to use the 6c potency twice daily for up to one month.

**Bach Flower Remedies** (see p. 12 for dosages and pp. 15–16 for administration)

WILLOW (*Salix vitellina*) is a little like STAPHYSAGRIA. Cats who are likely to benefit are those who harbour inner feelings of resentment, carrying a grudge against an intruder for months or even years and expressing their feelings by spraying zealously. Willow-cats feel very bitter and feel unjustly done by and may well develop aggressive traits as a result. Willow can unblock these feelings and make them think more positively about life. The result is a happier cat and the thankful cessation of spraying.

WALNUT (*Juglans regia*) Moving house is stressful for all concerned, including cats. For some, forced removal from familiar surroundings and established territory is just too much to cope with. Arrival and installation in the new house is greeted with contempt, ill-feeling and mounting anxiety. While many cats adapt well over a day or two, some are sufficiently intimidated to start spraying inside the house. This of course increases their self-confidence and feeling of security.

Walnut helps the transition and encourages the cat to come to terms with the current situation. It seems to work very well with STAPHYSAGRIA and if the situation is appropriate both can be given together.

There are a few instances of cats starting to spray when owners have redecorated or bought new furniture. The underlying psychological reasoning is the same: a feeling of insecurity, displeasure or indignation over the changes. It is worth trying STAPHYSAGRIA and WALNUT together. It may prevent your cat from ruining the new wallpaper!

CHICORY (*Cichorium intybus*) Cats who will benefit from this rule their owners' lives completely! Simply if they do not get their own way or their demands are not met instantly they spray. That is, spray not only their immediate surroundings but loving owners as well. They are really secret manipulators who demand full support at all times, sinking into self-pity or becoming angry if their whims are not fulfilled forthwith. Many would describe them as selfish. Chicory can remove this feeling and with it the desire to spray which was used only as a form of self-expression.

HEATHER (*Calluna vulgaris*) There is a distinct difference between cats who benefit from CHICORY and those who benefit from heather, which may not seem obvious at first. Where chicory centres around selfishness, heather-type cats are self-centred and, not only want to be the focus of attention, but let everybody else know about it as well – vocally! They dislike being alone and thrive on fuss and will absorb as much as they can be given with ease. However, if they do not get all that they demand or have to start sharing affection with another cat, they will tell you first and then start spraying in protest. Many Siamese are heather types, which is not surprising considering how talkative the breed can be.

LARCH (*Larix decidua*) An aggressive encounter with another cat can often leave the victim at a disadvantage, not only physically but mentally as well. The result is injured pride and the development of an inferiority complex. This increases the cat's anxiety level and the spraying threshold is exceeded. This means damp smelly patches around the house.

Cats who respond best to larch tend not to be the most robust. They are a little like the larch tree with its delicate leaves which rustle at the slightest breeze. Spraying of course boosts their confidence; however, this particular remedy brings out latent inherent energies, improving self-esteem and boosting ego and hopefully will stop the spraying.

MIMULUS (*Mimulus guttatus*) relates to specific fears whatever they may be and suits cats of a nervous, shy, timid nature. They generally spray to boost confidence. Typical fears and phobias include dogs, strangers, pieces of furniture, sudden noises and other cats. Mimulus seems to work quite well with larch for some cats.

---

*Thomas was a normal well-adjusted three-year-old Siamese. He was an 'only' cat and never ever sprayed until the day an intruder entered through the cat-flap unannounced. A frantic fight ensued with the rightful owner of the territory seeing off the foreigner, but not without a scratch or two.*

(cont.)

(cont.)

*From that day on, Thomas became a regular sprayer, partaking of the habit daily. We know the reasons behind this sudden change in behaviour but what could be done to put things right?*

STAPHYSAGRIA *was selected as the remedy of choice based on the feelings of resentment and indignation that Thomas undoubtedly felt. Over a period of about three weeks the number of spraying episodes gradually diminished and after five weeks had ceased altogether. The twice daily dose of Staphysagria 30 was stopped and all was well for five months when the unhygienic habit made a reappearance.*

*This time he sprayed when he could not get his own way, a bit like a selfish, attention-seeking child having a tantrum. If it was wet and cold and he could not go outside, Thomas sprayed. If his owners were having chicken for dinner and he did not get any, he sprayed. If they went out and left him, he sprayed. Staphysagria was prescribed again and helped a little but did not stop the problem altogether, so Bach flower remedies were added:* CHICORY *for his selfish nature and feelings of self-pity when he could not get his way,* HEATHER *for being self-centred and for being demanding on those around, and* WILLOW *for resentment. Two drops of each were added to his drinking water each day and within two weeks all was well once more.*

# Soiling Indoors

Almost all cats are by nature extremely clean animals, and once shown a litter tray, will always use that for preference, provided it is regularly cleaned. If your cat suddenly soils on the carpet or in an odd place, it may well be a cry for help, and it is worth examining whether something in particular has disrupted your cat's life (the decorators, moving furniture, a family row perhaps – or perhaps a change in the type of cat litter you are using), or whether perhaps your cat is feeling out of sorts, and consulting your vet.

*Barney-Buzzer, a large, six-year-old black and white neutered tom, normally attends to his toilet out-of-doors in the garden. However, a few months ago, he changed his habit and left his somewhat surprised owner a pile beside the plughole in the bath. Talking to B-B's original owner, Buzzer's master was told that the mother cat always did exactly this when she was not feeling well.*

*Buzzer was taken to the vet and found to have tartar which was causing toothache. Since his teeth were scraped and one decaying one removed, there has been no recurrence.*

# Cats Under Stress

Stress is a physiological response, that enables the body to cope with untoward situations. This involves the production of adrenalin as part of the flight or fight reaction which is essential to survival.

Any deviation from normal routine can produce stress in some cats, but there are basically two types of problems, first, short-lasting stressful situations such as car journeys, cat shows, trips in cat baskets, and traumatic experiences (accidents). In these situations natural remedies can help enormously. Signs of this type of stress are easily recognized. Look for sweaty pawprints on the table, panting and rapid breathing, salivation, crying out and excessive moulting. In more extreme situations the cat may panic and vomit food or inadvertently mess in the house or cat basket. Once the stress situation has passed, the cat returns to normal in an hour or so and there are no long-term consequences.

The second category includes those situations where stress causes long-term behavioural changes that can be disastrous for both owner and cat. Triggers can range from changes in lifestyle or daily routine (such as moving house), introduction of new animals into the household, delayed shock after trauma (such as being trapped in a room or garage), to noise sensitivity or intolerance of visitors.

Occasionally odd stress-related behaviour can be caused by reactions to food additives, which are largely unnecessary. Anti-oxidants, preservatives and artificial colours have been implicated. Feeding a basic home-cooked diet or one free from additives can certainly help some cats.

Typical responses to long-term stress states can include urine-spraying, inappropriate urination or defecation, destructive behaviour (clawing furniture), refusal to eat, self-mutilation by pulling out tufts of hair, psychogenic dermatitis and periodic vomiting. More obvious character changes are sometimes apparent, including symptoms of anxiety, tiredness, depression, ill-humour and irritability. Sudden alterations in behaviour such as these are understandably worrying and we are all aware that prolonged stress can cause real physical illness.

Always remember that playing with your cat can help it unwind, and so can stroking it and giving it attention and affection.

## HELPING SHORT-TERM STRESS SITUATIONS

*Pasta, a nervy, black neutered tom, and Biggles, a plump black and white female, regularly travel by car from town to country, a distance of some 250 miles. When the cat baskets are produced, Biggles appears to lose the use of her legs and sinks to the floor; Pasta races to the most inaccessible spot under the bed so that it has to be upturned to retrieve him. Once in the car, Biggles is soon asleep; Pasta, on the other hand, wails pathetically for at least 100 miles, then dozes fitfully until the car leaves the motorway, and the road begins to wind, when he invariably yowls loudly, and only a mile from his destination, evacuates at both ends. On arrival Biggles strides out unconcerned; Pasta, however, is a pathetic sight, panting and salivating. His owner now sprinkles dried catnip in her cats'*

(cont.)

(cont.)
*baskets. Pasta now sleeps throughout the journey and five
minutes after arrival is racing through the fields, eyes bright,
tail erect, as though nothing had ever happened.*

**Herbal Remedies** (see p. 5 for dosages, and pp. 15–16 for
administration)

VALERIAN (*Valeriana officinalis*) is well known for its calming
and sedative qualities. It is non-addictive and safe to use in
treating nervous cats, especially those who become excitable
and panic in stressful situations. Like most herbal remedies it
can be slow to act and works best if given a few days beforehand in anticipation of the problem.

SKULLCAP (*Scutellaria laterifolia*) is another herbal sedative that
is often combined with VALERIAN. It calms without causing
drowsiness and relieves anxiety and fear.

HOPS (*Humulus lupulus*) have a specific effect on the nervous
system, toning, relaxing and calming. They work well when
combined with SKULLCAP and VALERIAN.

**Homoeopathic Remedies** (see pp. 8–10 for dosages and
pp. 15–16 for administration)

ARNICA (Leopard's bane) is one of the best remedies to give
in cases of shock or injury. It works both on a mental and physical level, helping to calm the cat and limiting the effects of
any trauma by helping to stop bruising and reducing bleed-
ing. It works well where there is fear of being approached and
the cat would rather avoid human contact.

ACONITE (Monkshood) is the principal remedy for fear, sudden fright, shock and anguish. Use it where the cat appears restless, frantic and worried. Breathing may be rapid and there may be fear-induced salivation. If you know that your cat reacts this way in the car, anticipate the problem and give a few doses of aconite before leaving home.

GELSEMIUM (Yellow jasmine) is useful for car journeys and particularly for cats who get very worked up and frightened on visits to the vet. Fear is a feature, together with a desire to hide away and be left alone. This type of cat is very nearly petrified, fixed to the spot and so frightened that they may actually pass urine or faeces where they stand.

ARGENTUM NITRICUM (Silver nitrate) is linked with tense, nervous agitation and restlessness which distinguishes it from the GELSEMIUM-type cat. Excitement and panic result in involuntary urination or defecation. Fear of closed-in spaces (claustrophobia) and crowds of people are also useful indicators.

**Bach Flower Remedies** (see p. 12 for dosages and pp. 15–16 for administration)

RESCUE REMEDY is a combination of five remedies specifically for emergency situations and the most widely known of the Bach remedies. Its aim is to calm, reassure and comfort in times of stress where energy is draining from the body's resources. It can therefore initiate the healing process.

Rescue remedy includes STAR OF BETHLEHEM (for the ill-effects and fright associated with trauma), ROCK ROSE (for terror and panic), IMPATIENS (to quell anger and tension), CHERRY PLUM (to help maintain control and rational thinking) and CLEMATIS (to maintain links with reality and reduce the risk of unconsciousness).

Use it after accidents or injury (such as cat fights), for calming frightened animals, before car journeys or where the cat is likely to be upset for some reason, i.e. in anticipation of some forthcoming problem. In this situation add the remedy to the cat's drinking water a day or two before the problem is expected. In crisis situations give the remedy directly from the stock bottle (undiluted) straight into the mouth every fifteen to thirty minutes.

**Aromatherapy** (see pp. 13–14 for application)

One of the best ways of using some of the oils that can help is to sprinkle a few drops inside a cat basket. This works very well for poor travellers. Alternatively use the usual massage technique for dealing with the other problems.

LAVENDER (*Lavendula angustifolia*) is a safe, versatile oil and can help in many stress-related situations including anxiety, fear, tension, insecurity, irritability and worry.

GERANIUM (*Pelargonium graveolens*) helps balance the body on both physical and emotional levels and allows or assists adaptation to stressful situations. It can help with acute fear, anxiety and those cats which appear confused and worried.

CHAMOMILE (*Matricaria recutica*) Its calming properties make it an ideal remedy to use where stress leads to irritation, anger and aggression. It works particularly well when a few drops are used inside a cat basket before a journey.

CLARY SAGE (*Salvia sclarea*) Along with LAVENDER, clary sage is useful in helping those cats who are liable to panic and act irrationally, causing damage to themselves or others.

SANDALWOOD (*Santalum album*) helps relieve tension where it is related to forthcoming events and worry about the future. This includes situations such as the cat basket suddenly appearing from a cupboard, heralding a forthcoming trip (like it or not).


## TRAVEL SICKNESS

Use the following homoeopathic remedies (see pp. 8–10 for dosage and pp. 15–16 for administration)

COCCULUS (Indian cockle) is one of the main remedies for treating travel sickness. Cats sometimes will salivate and then vomit, even on short car journeys. Give a dose about half an hour before leaving home and then just before you go. Repeat doses can be given as necessary.

Where cocculus does not appear to work, try PETROLEUM (Crude rock oil). Salivation is very prominent with this remedy, more so than with cocculus.

Where travel sickness causes repeated vomiting try TABACUM (Tobacco). It is a good remedy to try where the cat vomits almost immediately after the start of the trip.


## OTHER STRESS-RELATED PROBLEMS

**Bach Flower Remedies** (see p. 12 for dosage and pp. 15–16 for administration)

Selfish and self-centred cats should respond to CHICORY (*Cichorium intybus*). These particular animals are possessive and expect the very best, almost constantly demanding attention or help. They have a strange way of manipulating their owners and all is well until they cannot get what they want or something occurs of which they disapprove. They are resentful of any change which will, or may potentially affect, their lives. Their sensitive unyielding nature is not able to cope with such problems easily, and the stress involved can lead to other difficulties.

Over-grooming is a typical reaction, and can lead to the development of dermatitis and hair loss (alopecia). Indulging in such behaviour is really a way of avoiding the problem by concentrating the mind elsewhere and perhaps a way of regaining the owner's full attention once more. This condition is sometimes referred to as psychogenic dermatitis and has been seen in cats, who react to a new arrival in the household. It has also occurred in response to owners going away on holiday, moving house or even after decorating! Taken to extremes it can lead to self-mutilation, especially to the tail area, and occasionally legs.

Chicory can also prove useful in solving problems such as indoor soiling, which can arise from stress, including such seemingly minor upsets such as moving furniture around or owners going away for a day or two. Part of the underlying problem in some cases is without doubt insecurity. Some of the remedies listed under Cowardly Cats (pp. 110–11) may well help.

RED CHESTNUT (*Aesculus carnea*) is useful in treating self-inflicted dermatitis or self-mutilation. The outstanding cause here is an overwhelming concern for the welfare or well-being of another animal or the owner. The worry can be so great in these anxious, sensitive animals that they will injure themselves as evidence of their frustration and concern.

WILLOW (*Salix vitellina*) is linked to feelings of resentment, and where feelings of selfishness (treatable with chicory) are not the underlying cause, then it may provide the answer. Such feelings are common among cats and can result in the development of any of the behavioural problems listed above.

Willow has been used successfully in the treatment of both over-grooming and strange undesirable changes in toileting behaviour as a result of resentment.

HEATHER (*Calluna vulgaris*) is a little like chicory in that they both relate to self-centred feelings. With heather the cat wants always to be the centre of attention and cannot bear being alone. They must have total commitment. Whereas 'chicory' cats wallow in self-pity when upset, heather-type cats rarely feel sorry for themselves. They are often very vocal when upset, letting everybody know their feelings. When there is no one to listen, then the feelings turn inward and changes in behaviour may ensue.

Peaceful, calm and controlled are words that typify the sort of cat who responds to AGRIMONY (*Agrimonia eupatoria*). Under the surface there may be turmoil, worry and frustration, all very well concealed. Such cats find it difficult to cope with stress and any upsets that cause mental strain, such as a new kitten suddenly appearing in the house. For a while they cope, maybe becoming a little less sociable and keeping themselves to themselves more and more as time goes by. Gradually the cat's character may change, becoming irritable and short-tempered. Even if outwardly nothing appears amiss, physical symptoms can mysteriously appear, ranging from hair loss to other skin problems such as over-grooming. Cats who benefit from agrimony keep their ill thoughts well behind a façade, but over a long period of time the stress of struggling against the worrying thoughts is just too much.

RESCUE REMEDY can be used to help cats cope with long-term stress, especially where there are suppressed feelings of worry or after trauma or fright.

Also try these homoeopathic remedies (see pp. 8–10 for dosages, pp. 15–16 for administration)

STAPHYSAGRIA (Stavesacre) is the most important homoeo-pathic remedy when dealing with stress-related behaviour problems. Its keynote is resentment or indignation and it is effective where these feelings lead to such conditions as psychogenic vomiting, over-grooming and associated skin problems or destructive behaviour. Cats who respond well are often angry and short-tempered and may spend part of the time just grumbling and feeling ill-humoured. This behaviour is especially noticeable if it appears in a cat who is normally gentle and placid. There is more about this remedy in the section on resentment pp. 105–8.

ANACARDIUM (Marking nut) has helped cure psychogenic eczema where there has been intense itching of the skin asso-ciated with a rash. Lack of confidence and poor memory are probably responsible for part of the problem. This sort of cat is usually unhappy and inclined to fits of rage and may bite if provoked.

Where insecurity is suspected as the root of the problem try BRYONIA (White bryony). Insecure cats are the ones who mess in the house when you go out. By doing this they probably feel more secure by surrounding themselves with their own smell. The only problem is that they nearly always do this in specific areas, often those which smell the strongest of the owner, because this increases their sense of security in the owner's absence.

The 'bryonia' type of cat is often difficult anyway and some-what pig-headed. They are prone to become angry or depressed if they are unable to get their own way or if any-thing upsets their stable lives. Consequently they are anxious individuals who dislike being disturbed.

# List of Suppliers

**All the Best**
8047 Lake City Way
Seattle, WA 98115
1-800-962-8266
Natural pet foods, supplements,
homeopathics, supplies

**American Holistic Veterinary
Medical Association**
2214 Old Emmorton Rd.
Bel Air, MD 21014
(301) 838-7778
Referrals and information

**Amrita Herbal Products**
Rt, 1, Box 737
Floyd, VA 24091
(703) 745-3474
Herb tinctures and salves

**Beckett's Apothecary**
1004 Chester Pike
Sharon Hill, PA 19079
1-800-727-8188
Homeopathic remedies
mail order

**Boericke and Tafel**
1011 Arch St.
Philadelphia, PA 19107
1-800-272-2820
Homeopathic pharmacy, mail
order homeopathics

**Coyote Moon Herbs**
Teresa Finkbeiner, MH
P.O. Box 312
Gainesville, FL 32602
(904) 377-0765
Herbs, Mail Order

**Dr. Goodpet Laboratories**
P.O. Box 4489
Inglewood, CA 90309
(213) 672-3269, 1-800-222-9932
Homeopathics and vitamins

**Ellon Bach USA, Inc.**
644 Merrick Rd.
Lynbrook, NY 11563
1-800-433-7523
Bach flower remedies

**Flower Essence Society**
P.O. Box 459
Nevada City, CA 95959
1-800-548-0075
Flower essences, aromatherapy,
books

**Standard Homeopathic Co.**
P.O. Box 61067
Los Angeles, CA 90061
(310) 321-4284, 1-800-624-9659
Homeopathic remedies and
books

# Index